Illuminate Publishing

WJEC
Chemistry
A2 Level

Study and Revision Guide

David Ballard
Rhodri Thomas

ip

Published in 2017 by Illuminate Publishing Ltd, P.O Box 1160, Cheltenham, Gloucestershire GL50 9RW

Orders: Please visit www.illuminatepublishing.com or email sales@illuminatepublishing.com

British Library Cataloguing in Publication Data

A catalogue record for this book is available from the British Library

ISBN 978-1-908682-57-4

Printed by Ashford Colour Press, Gosport

02.19

The publisher's policy is to use papers that are natural, renewable and recyclable products made from wood grown in sustainable forests. The logging and manufacturing processes are expected to conform to the environmental regulations of the country of origin.

Every effort has been made to contact copyright holders of material reproduced in this book. If notified, the publishers will be pleased to rectify any errors or omissions at the earliest opportunity.

This material has been endorsed by WJEC and offers high quality support for the delivery of WJEC qualifications. While this material has been through a WJEC quality assurance process, all responsibility for the content remains with the publisher.

WJEC examination questions are reproduced by permission from WJEC

Editor: Claire Eudall
Design: Nigel Harriss
Layout: EMC Design Ltd, Bedford

Acknowledgements

We are very grateful to the team at Illuminate Publishing for their professionalism, support and guidance throughout this project. It has been a pleasure to work so closely with them.

The authors and publisher wish to thank:

Judith Bonello for her thorough review of the book and expert insights and observations.

Contents

How to use this book   4

Knowledge and Understanding

Unit 3   Physical and Inorganic Chemistry

3.1 Redox and standard electrode potential   8
3.2 Redox reactions   13
3.3 Chemistry of the p-block   16
3.4 Chemistry of the d-block transition elements   24
3.5 Chemical kinetics   27
3.6 Enthalpy changes for solids and solutions   30
3.7 Entropy and feasibility of reactions   32
3.8 Equilibrium constants   34
3.9 Acid-base equilibria   38

Unit 4   Organic chemistry and analysis

4.1 Stereoisomerism   48
4.2 Aromaticity   50
4.3 Alcohols and phenols   54
4.4 Aldehydes and ketones   57
4.5 Carboxylic acids and their derivatives   60
4.6 Amines   65
4.7 Amino acids, peptides and proteins   69
4.8 Organic synthesis and analysis   70

Unit 5   Practical Work

Experimental task   81
Practical paper   81

Exam practice and technique

Exam practice and skills   82
Q and A   85
Quickfire answers   124
Unit 4 Extra answers   125
Index   126

How to use this book

As experienced senior examiners for the WJEC Chemistry specification, we have written this study guide to help you be aware of what is required, and structured the content to guide you through to success in the GCE Chemistry examination. The book is divided into two main sections, for Unit 3 and for Unit 4.

Knowledge and understanding

The **first section** of the book covers the key knowledge and understanding that is required for the examination and provides notes for each of the two examination theory papers, as well as some comments about the practical examination, Unit 5.

In addition we have tried to give you pointers that will help you with your learning.

- Questions may be based on certain terms in the specification, so these are defined and highlighted.

- There are 'Quickfire' questions designed to test your knowledge and understanding of the material.

- 'Pointers' pick out things that may be useful in answering questions.

- 'Grade Boost' inserts point out key ways in which candidates can impress the examiners by their knowledge and understanding.

- 'Extra' comprises a type of 'Quickfire' question that increases in difficulty.

- There is a comprehensive set of candidates' answers to questions in all sections, along with marking, analysis and explanation by the examiners, of these answers.

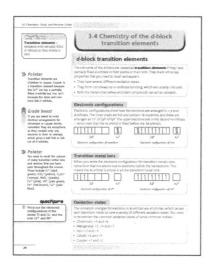

Exam practice and techniques

The **second section** covers the key skills needed for examination success and gives examples of responses to examination questions. We begin by giving you an insight into the examination itself, and how it is assessed, and then offering clues to success.

A variety of questions are provided. Most of these are structured style questions with a few longer answer questions. This reflects the form of the examination. Each question presents you with two typical candidate answers with comments about their performance. Questions for Unit 3 tend to be focused on an individual topic whereas the questions for Unit 4 tend to cover a range of topics, as seen in the actual examinations.

We advise you to seek out and learn from a number of sources and not to just rely on a particular book and the notes from your teachers.

Try to make good use of the WJEC website www.wjec.co.uk, where you will find specimen papers and their mark schemes, and, as time goes on, the actual papers that were set in previous years. This new specification has more emphasis on the **application** of your knowledge and understanding and there is less dependence on recall questions than in the past. In addition, there will be more questions that require the use of mathematics.

We hope that you find this book useful in your studies and that it helps you to gain the grades that will enable you to advance onto the next level of your career.

David Ballard and Rhodri Thomas

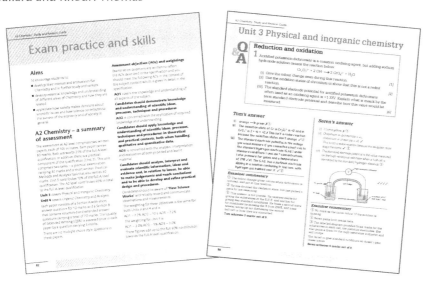

U3

Knowledge and Understanding

Physical and Inorganic Chemistry

This unit builds on ideas studied in both units in year 1 of the course. Many topics within this unit rely on a firm understanding and recall of year 1 ideas and you may find it useful to review the year 1 topic before starting your study of the year 2 content.

This unit examines how the behaviour of matter can be studied and described mathematically. This allows us to predict which reactions are feasible and the stability of substances using ideas of enthalpy and entropy. We can predict how far reactions will progress using ideas of equilibria and how fast they will occur using the ideas of rates. Electrochemistry allows us to study the properties of redox reactions and explain the behaviour of batteries and fuel cells.

Inorganic chemistry classifies the behaviour of a wide range of elements, with all compounds except those based on hydrocarbons being in this category. The behaviour of elements of the *p*-block are exemplified by the compounds and reactions of elements in groups 3, 4 and 7. The behaviour of elements of the *d*-block are exemplified by the compounds and reactions of elements in the first row of the transition elements.

Revised it!

3.1 Redox and standard electrode potential

Redox reactions can be undertaken in electrochemical cells which separate reduction and oxidation reactions. This allows the oxidising power of each half-cell to be measured using the standard electrode potential by comparison with the standard hydrogen electrode. Any cell can be represented by a cell diagram and its EMF can be measured and used to assess the feasibility of reaction. Fuel cells use electrochemical principles to release the energy very efficiently.

3.2 Redox reactions

Redox reactions can be used in titrations. These allow the concentrations of a wide range of substances to be assessed. The titration for Cu^{2+} ions is undertaken in two steps with the Cu^{2+} used to produce iodine which is then analysed in a titration with thiosulfate.

3.3 Chemistry of the *p*-block

The arrangement of electrons in the *p*-block elements governs their patterns of behaviour. The oxidation states of these elements are affected by the inert pair effect and octet expansion, as well as the trends to metallic behaviour down the group. Group 3 elements form many electron deficient species, as well as analogues for the allotropes of carbon. Group 4 elements show very different behaviour due to the significant variation in the inert pair effect and metallic properties down the group. Group 7 elements and compounds show trends in reactions based on the stability of their oxidation states.

3.4 Chemistry of the *d*-block transition metals

The *d*-block elements show similar properties such as their abilities to form variable oxidation states and complexes with ligands. The complexes of copper and cobalt are used as examples. Complexes are usually coloured and can often act as catalysts. All these compounds in solution react with sodium hydroxide, with the amphoteric metals behaving differently to the others.

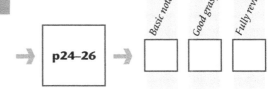

Basic notes   *Good grasp*   *Fully revised*

p24–26

3.5 Chemical kinetics

In year 1 the effects of concentration and temperature were studied qualitatively, but in this topic, the effects are quantified. The effects of concentration changes are used to produce the rate equation, with the Arrhenius equation used to explain the way rate changes with temperature. The rate equation can be used to find out about the mechanism of a chemical reaction.

p27–29

3.6 Enthalpy changes for solids and solutions

Energy changes can be calculated using Hess's Law. These changes can be broken down into many small steps that need to be recalled and understood such as atomisation, lattice formation, hydration, ionisation energy and electron affinity. Combining these together into an energy cycle allows the stability or solubility of ionic compounds to be calculated.

p30–31

3.7 Entropy and feasibility of reactions

Entropy is a measure of the freedom or disorder of a system, and it increases from ordered solids to liquids then gases. Entropy must increase overall in any change, and the effects of the entropy change of a reaction and the surroundings are combined in the Gibbs free energy. The Gibbs free energy for any change must be negative for the reaction to be feasible.

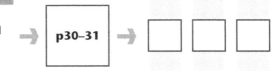

p32–33

3.8 Equilibrium constants

The position of any equilibrium can be described using the concentrations or partial pressures of all substances present. These are combined to form the equilibrium constants K_p and K_c, which can be applied to any equilibrium mixtures to find the amounts of any substance present. The values of K_p and K_c give a qualitative idea of the position of equilibrium.

p34–37

3.9 Acid-base equilibria

The equilibrium constants K_a and K_w are key to finding the pH of weak acids and strong bases. The salts of weak acids and of weak bases are not neutral. Buffers are formed from mixtures of weak acids and their salts and their pH depends on the K_a of the acid and the concentrations of the acid and salt. During titrations, the pH changes and the pH curves depend on the strength of the acids and bases used. The selection of the correct indicator depends on the shape of the titration curve.

p38–43

3.1 Redox and standard electrode potential

Redox reactions

In redox reactions, something is oxidised and something else is reduced. These processes can be defined in terms of electrons or in terms of oxidation states.

Grade boost

If you are asked to identify oxidation or reduction then clearly state the oxidation state of the atom at the start of the reaction and at the end of the reaction and then state whether it has been oxidised (more positive), reduced (more negative) or neither (no change).

≫ Pointer

Oxidising agents become reduced as they oxidise something else.
Reducing agents become oxidised as they reduce something else.

≫ Pointer

Do not mix up charges and oxidation states – they are similar but not the same: +3 and −2 are oxidation states but 3+ and 2− are charges.

quickⱯire

① Work out the oxidation states of the atoms underlined in the following list: $\underline{S}_8$, $\underline{Fe}^{3+}$, $Na\underline{Cl}$, $\underline{H}_2O$, $\underline{F}_2O$, $Ca\underline{H}_2$, $Al\underline{Cl}_4^-$, $NaO\underline{Cl}$, $Na\underline{I}O_3$, $\underline{Mn}O_4^-$.

Oxidation states

Oxidation states measure how much an atom has been oxidised compared with the element. Oxidation states allow us to measure **oxidation** and **reduction** in covalent compounds as well as ionic compounds. The oxidation state of an atom is:

0 in elements, e.g. in Xe, O_2, C_{60}.

Equal to the charge in ions, e.g. +2 in Fe^{2+}.

Negative for the most electronegative atom in a compound.

+1 for group 1 metals in compounds and +2 for group 2 metals in compounds.

+1 for hydrogen, except in metal hydrides where it is −1.

−1 for fluorine in its compounds.

−2 for oxygen in its compounds except in peroxides where it is −1.

−1 for halogens in metal halides.

The sum of all the oxidation states of atoms in a compound equals the charge on the species – for a neutral species the sum equals zero.

Oxidation is where oxidation states become more positive; reduction is where oxidation states become less positive or more negative.

Examples

$$Cr_2O_7^{2-} + 14\ H^+ + 6\ Fe^{2+} \longrightarrow 2\ Cr^{3+} + 6\ Fe^{3+} + 7\ H_2O$$

Orange   Green

The oxidation state of chromium in the reactants is +6, and in the products it is +3. The chromium has been reduced – we say it is an oxidising agent.

When we add an alkali (e.g. sodium hydroxide) to a solution containing dichromate(VI) ions, the reaction below occurs:

$$Cr_2O_7^{2-} + 2\ OH^- \longrightarrow 2\ CrO_4^{2-} + H_2O$$

Orange   Yellow

The oxidation state of chromium in the reactants is +6, and in the products it is +6. It has not been oxidised or reduced – this is not a redox reaction.

Equations and half-equations

In a redox reaction, one species is being reduced and another is being oxidised. We can usually divide a full chemical equation into two half-equations, one showing the oxidation and one showing the reduction. In the example below, the Cu^{2+} (aq) is being reduced and the Mg (s) is being oxidised:

$$Cu^{2+} (aq) + Mg (s) \longrightarrow Cu (s) + Mg^{2+} (aq)$$

The Cu^{2+} (aq) is converted into Cu (s). To do this it must have gained two electrons so the ion-electron half-equation is:

$$Cu^{2+} (aq) + 2e^- \longrightarrow Cu (s)$$

The Mg (s) is converted into Mg^{2+} (aq). To do this it must have lost two electrons so the ion-electron half-equation is:

$$Mg (s) \longrightarrow Mg^{2+} (aq) + 2e^-$$

Electrochemical cells

Half-equations are not just a theory – it is possible to separate a redox reaction so oxidation happens in one place and reduction happens somewhere else. To do this we need to set up two half-cells where the separate processes will happen, and join them together in a complete circuit.

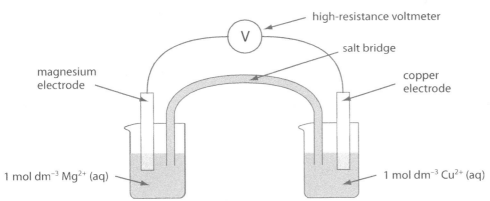

Mg(s)|Mg²⁺(aq)||Cu²⁺(aq)|Cu(s) cell

The high-resistance voltmeter gives a reading of the EMF produced by the cell. The salt bridge completes the circuit by allowing ions to move, without the two solutions mixing.

>> Pointer

Do not mix up a diagram of an electrochemical cell with a cell diagram. A cell diagram is a representation of a cell written in one line of text and not a drawing.

Grade boost

When writing cell diagrams, put the metals at both ends, with a salt bridge in the middle (shown by two vertical lines, ||). A vertical line shows each change of state, with a comma between species in the same physical state. The metal with the most negative E^θ goes on the left.

>> Pointer

If you need to label a diagram of a cell fully, you'll need to remember that the half-cell with the most positive E^θ value <u>will be the positive electrode</u>, and electrons flow along the wire towards this half-cell.

Key Term

Standard electrode potential (E^θ) = the potential difference when any half-cell is connected to the standard hydrogen electrode under standard conditions.

Standard electrode potentials, E^θ

Each electrochemical cell has a different tendency to gain or lose electrons. It is useful to have a way to measure and compare these and so we use the **standard electrode potential (E^θ)**. To measure the value of E^θ for any half-cell, we need to connect it to the standard hydrogen electrode under standard conditions, and measure the potential difference using a high-resistance voltmeter.

Standard hydrogen electrode

The standard hydrogen electrode is a half-cell where H_2 gas at a pressure of 1 atm bubbles over an inert platinum electrode dipped in 1 mol dm^{-3} H$^+$ (aq) at a temperature of 298 K.

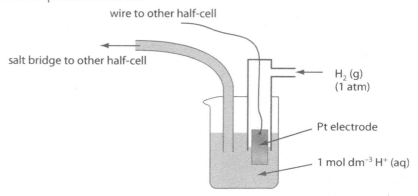

⚑ Grade boost

Remember to be clear if you are asked to label a diagram of a cell – the voltmeter must be a high-resistance voltmeter and always specify the metal used to make the electrode. Always include the standard conditions:
1 mol dm^{-3} for the concentrations of solutions
1 atm for the pressures of gas
298 K for the temperature.

This is the standard half-cell which all others are compared to. Its standard electrode potential is defined as being exactly 0 volts.

We can measure the standard electrode potentials for three types of half-cell:

A metal–solution half-cell: A piece of metal acting as an electrode dipping into a solution containing ions of the same metal. Examples include Cu | Cu^{2+} and Zn | Zn^{2+}.

A gas–solution half-cell: A gas is bubbled over an inert platinum electrode dipping in a solution containing ions of the gas. Examples include the standard hydrogen electrode and X_2 (g) | X$^-$ (aq) (X=Cl, Br or I).

A mixed ion half-cell: This half-cell also uses an inert platinum electrode. We place this electrode in a solution containing different ions of the same element in different oxidation states. Examples include Fe^{2+}, Fe^{3+} and Mn^{2+}, MnO$_4^-$. Note that commas are used here as both ions are in the same physical state.

A cell diagram for these two half-cells joined together would be
Pt | Fe^{2+}, Fe^{3+} || MnO$_4^-$, Mn^{2+} | Pt.

quickfire

② Draw a labelled diagram to show the electrochemical cell that should be used to measure the standard electrode potential for the following reaction:

Fe^{3+} (aq) + e $\longrightarrow$ Fe^{2+} (aq).

Using standard electrode potentials

Some common standard electrode values, along with some of the associated colour changes are listed below:

E^θ / V

Zn^{2+} (aq) + 2e$^-$ $\rightleftharpoons$ Zn (s)　　　　−0.76

2 H$^+$ (aq) + 2e$^-$ $\rightleftharpoons$ H$_2$ (g)　　　　0.00

Cu^{2+} (aq) + 2e$^-$ $\rightleftharpoons$ Cu (s)　　　　+0.34
Blue

I$_2$ (aq) + 2 e$^-$ $\rightleftharpoons$ 2 I$^-$ (aq)　　　　+0.54

Fe^{3+} (aq) + e$^-$ $\rightleftharpoons$ Fe^{2+} (aq)　　　　+0.77
Yellow　　　　　　Pale green

Br$_2$ (aq) + 2 e$^-$ $\rightleftharpoons$ 2 Br$^-$ (aq)　　　　+1.09
Orange　　　　　　Colourless

$Cr_2O_7^{2-}$ (aq) + 14 H$^+$(aq) + 6e$^-$ $\rightleftharpoons$ 2 Cr^{3+} (aq) + 7H$_2$O(l)　　　+1.33
Orange　　　　　　　　　　　　Dark green

Cl$_2$ (aq) + 2 e$^-$ $\rightleftharpoons$ 2 Cl$^-$ (aq)　　　　+1.36

MnO_4^- (aq) + 8 H$^+$ (aq) + 5e$^-$ $\rightleftharpoons$ Mn^{2+} (aq) + 4 H$_2$O(l)　　+1.51
Purple　　　　　　　　　　Pale pink/
　　　　　　　　　　　　　colourless

The more positive the value of the E^θ the more likely the system is to gain electrons. If you connect two half-cells together, electrons will flow from the more negative half-cell to the more positive one. The reading on the high-resistance voltmeter will be given by:

Standard potential of cell = E^θ (more positive) – E^θ (less positive)

Is a reaction feasible?

We can use the E^θ values to work out if a reaction is feasible. For a reaction to be possible, the EMF for the reaction must be positive. To calculate the EMF, we need to identify which half-equation is the reduction and which is the oxidation.

EMF = E^θ for reduction – E^θ for oxidation

For example, we can identify whether chloride can reduce Cu^{2+} ions to copper metal using the E^θ values above. The two relevant half-equations are:

Cu^{2+} (aq) + 2e$^-$ $\rightleftharpoons$ Cu (s)　　　　+0.34 V

Cl$_2$ (aq) + 2 e$^-$ $\rightleftharpoons$ 2 Cl$^-$ (aq)　　　　+1.36 V

This reaction involves Cu^{2+} $\longrightarrow$ Cu, which is a reduction, and Cl$^-$ $\longrightarrow$ Cl$_2$, which is an oxidation. The EMF for the reaction is:

EMF = E^θ for Cu^{2+} – E^θ for Cl$^-$ = 0.34 – 1.36 = −1.02 V

The reaction is not feasible as the standard potential is negative.

Grade boost

When discussing oxidation and reduction, it is important to make sure that you clearly identify any species involved. A common error is to confuse iodide and iodine, or to mix up metal atoms.
If asked to identify the strongest reducing agent, then you need to say that this is the zinc atom or zinc metal not just zinc as this could be the Zn^{2+} ion.

quickfire

③ Calculate the standard potentials that would be measured if the following pairs of half-cells were connected together:
a) Zn | Zn^{2+} and Cu | Cu^{2+}.
b) Zn | Zn^{2+} and Fe^{2+}, Fe^{3+} | Pt.

quickfire

④ Use the values of E^θ given to show that bromide ions will react with Cl$_2$ but not with I$_2$.

Uses of redox reactions

Redox reactions are very common in chemistry. You have seen many redox reactions in previous units, but they are also common in industry, where metals are extracted from their ores; in biology, respiration and photosynthesis both involve a complex series of reductions and oxidations.

Redox reactions in organic synthesis

You have seen the use of reduction and oxidation in your work in other units. These include:

- Oxidation of alcohols to aldehydes, ketones or carboxylic acids using acidified potassium dichromate(VI).
- Reduction of nitriles to amines or reduction of carboxylic acids, aldehydes and ketones to alcohols using lithium tetrahydridoaluminate(III).
- Reduction of nitrobenzene and its derivatives to phenylamines using tin and hydrochloric acid.

Grade boost

Make sure you can recall at least one advantage and at least one disadvantage of fuel cells and express these clearly.
Common errors are to use vague answers such as 'less pollution' or 'gases are harmless'.

Fuel cells

Fuel cells use electrochemical methods to get energy from fuels, typically hydrogen gas. At one platinum electrode, hydrogen is oxidised to H^+ ions, whilst at the other platinum electrode, oxygen gas is reduced to water, H_2O:

$$\text{At the anode} \quad H_2 \longrightarrow 2H^+ + 2e^-$$

$$\text{At the cathode} \quad O_2 + 4H^+ + 4e^- \longrightarrow 2H_2O$$

The overall reaction that occurs is: $2H_2 + O_2 \longrightarrow 2H_2O$.

This method of obtaining energy has many advantages and disadvantages.

Advantages

- Water is the only product, so no carbon dioxide (a greenhouse gas) is produced.
- Highly efficient, as less energy is wasted as heat, so much more energy is used effectively.
- Hydrogen gas can be produced using renewable resources by the electrolysis of water.

Disadvantages

- Hydrogen gas is highly flammable and difficult to store.
- Hydrogen gas is usually produced from fossil fuels, which leads to a net energy loss.

3.2 Redox reactions

In a redox reaction both oxidation and reduction occur together, so to work out the overall equation by combining two half-equations, one written as a reduction and one as an oxidation, both equations must contain the same number of electrons.

Example: $Cr_2O_7^{2-}$ reacting with Fe^{2+}.

The two relevant half-equations for this reaction are:

$$Cr_2O_7^{2-} (aq) + 14 H^+(aq) + 6e^- \longrightarrow 2 Cr^{3+} (aq) + 7 H_2O (l)$$
$$Fe^{3+} (aq) + e^- \longrightarrow Fe^{2+} (aq)$$

Both these are reductions as written above, but as we are starting with Fe^{2+} (aq) rather than Fe^{3+} (aq) we need to reverse the second reaction to make it into an oxidation:

$$Fe^{2+} (aq) \longrightarrow Fe^{3+} (aq) + e^-$$

To get the same number of electrons in each we must multiply this by 6 to give:

$$6 Fe^{2+} (aq) \longrightarrow 6 Fe^{3+} (aq) + 6 e^-$$

Then we add both equations together, and then cancel out the electrons and anything else that is present in both reactants and products:

$$Cr_2O_7^{2-} + 14 H^+ + 6 e^- + 6 Fe^{2+} \longrightarrow 2 Cr^{3+} + 7 H_2O + 6 Fe^{3+} + 6 e^-$$
$$Cr_2O_7^{2-} + 14 H^+ + 6 Fe^{2+} \longrightarrow 2 Cr^{3+} + 7 H_2O + 6 Fe^{3+}$$

In this example we must cancel out electrons only, but if there are any other species such as H^+ that are the same on both sides of the equation then these are cancelled out as well.

Redox titrations

You should be familiar with the technique of titration from your previous work in the AS course. Most redox titrations are carried out in the same way as acid-base titrations, except that an indicator is not always needed as the colours of the reactants allow the end point to be seen.

>> **Pointer**

You do not need to include state symbols like (s) or (aq) unless the question specifically asks you to.

>> **Pointer**

The titrations undertaken in the first year of the course will help when performing redox titrations. These skills can be examined in unit 3 but also in both the unit 5 assessments.

quicKfire

⑤ Write a balanced equation for the oxidation of Cl^- by acidified MnO_4^-.

≫ Pointer

Any calculation from unit 1 could appear in the unit 3 paper, including interconverting masses and moles, reacting masses, atom economies or percentage yields.

quickfire

⑥ A 1.252g sample of an iron alloy was dissolved in acid. The Fe^{2+} solution formed required 21.40 cm³ of potassium manganate(VII) of concentration 0.200 mol dm⁻³ for complete reaction. Calculate the mass of iron present in the alloy. Use this to find the percentage of iron in the alloy.

Oxidation of Fe^{2+} by acidified manganate(VII), MnO_4^-

In the case of a titration involving potassium manganate(VII), this purple solution is added from the burette. When it reacts it forms Mn^{2+}, which is almost colourless. At the end point, the solution goes pale pink because some of the purple MnO_4^- remains, which appears pink when dilute.

If we need to do calculations based on a titration like this one, we need to know the reacting ratio (the stoichiometry). This is usually taken straight from the chemical equation. For this titration, the equation is:

$$MnO_4^- + 8\ H^+ + 5\ Fe^{2+} \longrightarrow Mn^{2+} + 4\ H_2O + 5\ Fe^{3+}$$

This means that the reacting ratio is $1\ MnO_4^- \equiv 5\ Fe^{2+}$.

All titration calculations rely on the same mathematical equations. Since all volumes in titration calculation use volumes of cm³, the number of moles can be calculated using:

$$\text{Number of moles} = \text{Concentration (in mol dm}^{-3}) \times \frac{\text{Volume (in cm}^3)}{1000}$$

Example question: A solution of Fe^{2+} (aq) is titrated against acidified potassium manganate(VII). A 25.00 cm³ sample of Fe^{2+} (aq) required 23.80 cm³ of a potassium manganate(VII) solution of concentration 0.0200 mol dm⁻³ for complete reaction. Calculate the number of moles of Fe^{2+} (aq) present in the sample.

To answer this, we need to calculate the number of moles of manganate(VII) using the equation above, then use the reacting ratio to calculate the number of moles of Fe^{2+} (aq) that would react with this.

$$\text{Moles } MnO_4^- = 0.0200 \text{ mol dm}^{-3} \times \frac{23.80 \text{ cm}^3}{1000} = 4.76 \times 10^{-4} \text{ moles}$$

Since $1\ MnO_4^- \equiv 5\ Fe^{2+}$ then $4.76 \times 10^{-4}\ MnO_4^- \equiv \underline{2.38 \times 10^{-3} \text{ moles } Fe^{2+}}$

Oxidation of Fe^{2+} by acidified dichromate(VI), $Cr_2O_7^{2-}$

In this reaction, potassium dichromate(VI) turns from orange to green as it oxidises the Fe^{2+}. The reaction is:

$$Cr_2O_7^{2-} + 14\ H^+ + 6\ Fe^{2+} \longrightarrow 2\ Cr^{3+} + 7\ H_2O + 6\ Fe^{3+}$$

This means that the reacting ratio is $1\ Cr_2O_7^{2-} \equiv 6\ Fe^{2+}$.

Finding Cu^{2+} by reduction of iodine by thiosulfate, $S_2O_3^{2-}$

We can't measure Cu^{2+} concentration directly but if we add iodide ions to a solution, a white solid of CuI and a brown solution of iodine, I_2 (aq) are formed:

$$2\ Cu^{2+}\ (aq) + 4\ I^-\ (aq) \longrightarrow 2\ CuI\ (s) + I_2\ (aq)$$

We can then add sodium thiosulfate solution from a burette to reduce the iodine:

$$I_2 + 2\ S_2O_3^{2-} \longrightarrow 2\ I^- + S_4O_6^{2-}$$

This causes the solution to become much paler until it is straw coloured. A starch indicator is then added which is blue-black in the presence of iodine. The end point of the reaction is when the blue-black colour of the starch becomes colourless. We often describe the final mixture as appearing flesh-coloured.

We need to work out a reacting ratio that links together Cu^{2+} and $S_2O_3^{2-}$. From the equations above we can see that:

$$2\ Cu^{2+} \equiv 1\ I_2 \qquad \text{and} \qquad 1\ I_2 \equiv 2\ S_2O_3^{2-}$$

We can combine these to show that $2\ Cu^{2+} \equiv 2\ S_2O_3^{2-}$ so $1\ Cu^{2+} \equiv 1\ S_2O_3^{2-}$

quickfire

⑦ An excess of potassium iodide solution was added to 25.00 cm³ of copper(II) sulfate solution, and the iodine released required 30.25 cm³ of a sodium thiosulfate of concentration 0.248 mol dm⁻³ for complete reaction. Calculate the concentration of the copper(II) sulfate solution.

Quick calculations

If you are asked to calculate a concentration or volume from other volumes and concentrations, you can do this directly using:

$$\frac{C_1 \times V_1}{C_2 \times V_2} = \frac{n_1}{n_2}$$

where C is the concentration, V is the volume and n is the number in the reacting ratio for each substance.

Example question: 25.00 cm³ of a solution of Fe^{2+}(aq) required 24.45 cm³ of a potassium dichromate(VI) solution of concentration 0.0200 mol dm⁻³ for complete reaction. Calculate the concentration of Fe^{2+} (aq) in the solution.

Answer: The reacting ratio in this case is $1\ Cr_2O_7^{2-} \equiv 6\ Fe^{2+}$. Using Fe^{2+} as substance 1 and $Cr_2O_7^{2-}$ as substance 2 we have:

$$\frac{C_{Fe} \times V_{Fe}}{C_{Cr} \times V_{Cr}} = \frac{n_{Fe}}{n_{Cr}} \qquad \text{rearranges to} \qquad C_{Fe} = \frac{n_{Fe} \times C_{Cr} \times V_{Cr}}{n_{Cr} \times V_{Fe}}$$

$$\text{So: } C_{Fe} = \frac{6 \times 0.0200 \times 24.45}{1 \times 25.00} = 0.117 \text{ mol dm}^{-3}$$

» Pointer

When we write 'n' in an electronic configuration we mean the period number so a group 3 element in period 2 would be $2s^2 2p^1$ and for period 4 would be $4s^2 4p^1$.

1 Write equations for the reactions of $Al(OH)_3$ with an acid (either as H^+ or HNO_3) and a base (either as OH^- or NaOH).

Write equations for the reactions of PbO with an acid (either as H^+ or HNO_3) and a base (either as OH^- or NaOH).

Grade boost

When writing the reactions of any lead compounds with acid, you must use nitric acid or ethanoic acid. Other acids form insoluble lead (II) salts which coat the reactant and prevent further reaction.

3.3 Chemistry of the *p*-block

Principles of *p*-block chemistry

The *p*-block is the area of the periodic table where elements have their outermost electrons in *p*-orbitals. You will need to recall and understand the chemistry of groups 3, 4 and 7, and they share some key properties:

- electronic configurations with partially filled *p*-orbitals;
- amphoteric behaviour for some *p*-block metals;
- oxidation states which vary due to octet expansion and the inert pair effect.

Electronic configurations

Electronic configurations show how the electrons are arranged in *s*, *p* and *d*-orbitals. The electronic configurations for the *p*-block elements have their outermost electrons in *p*-orbitals. A group 3 element will have a total of three electrons in its *s* and *p*-orbitals, group 4 will have four electrons in these orbitals and group 7 will have seven electrons. These are arranged as shown below.

ns^2 np^1 · ns^2 np^2 · ns^2 np^5

Electronic configuration for group 3 · *Electronic configuration for group 4* · *Electronic configuration for group 7*

Amphoteric behaviour

Many of the *p*-block metals are **amphoteric**. You are expected to be able to describe chemical reactions that show this, including both observations and equations.

Two examples of amphoteric metals are lead and aluminium. If you add sodium hydroxide to solutions of lead(II) nitrate or aluminium nitrate, you will see a white precipitate that will dissolve when more sodium hydroxide is added, giving a colourless solution.

Reactions of sodium hydroxide with Al^{3+}:

$$Al^{3+}\ (aq) + 3\ OH^-\ (aq) \longrightarrow Al(OH)_3\ (s)$$
$$Al(OH)_3\ (s) + OH^-\ (aq) \longrightarrow [Al(OH)_4]^-\ (aq)$$

Reactions of sodium hydroxide with Pb^{2+}:

$$Pb^{2+}\ (aq) + 2\ OH^-\ (aq) \longrightarrow Pb(OH)_2\ (s)$$
$$Pb(OH)_2\ (s) + 2\ OH^-\ (aq) \longrightarrow [Pb(OH)_4]^{2-}\ (aq)$$

Oxidation states

The highest oxidation state the *p*-block elements can reach should equal their group number, so a group 3 element could reach a +3 oxidation state and a group 4 element could reach a +4 oxidation state. Two factors affect whether these elements can reach these maximum values: octet expansion and the **inert pair** effect.

Octet expansion

For compounds in groups 5 or 6 to form their highest oxidation states, they would need 5 or 6 covalent bonds giving 10 or 12 electrons in their outer shell. To fit all these electrons into a shell, we need to use *s*, *p* and *d*-orbitals. This is not a problem for the third period onwards as *d*-orbitals are available, and we say these elements can form more bonds because they can expand their octet by using the *d*-orbitals.

The second period elements (N and O) don't have any available *d*-orbitals so we say these elements cannot expand their octets, so they can only have 8 electrons in their outer shells. This limits nitrogen to three covalent bonds and oxygen to two covalent bonds.

Inert pair effect

All the *p*-block elements have a pair of electrons in the *s*-orbital, as well as electrons in their *p*-orbitals and most of the elements use all these electrons during bonding. As you go down the groups, the ns^2 pair of electrons are less able to be involved in bonding, and we call them an inert pair.

This makes the elements lower in the group show an oxidation state 2 lower than the group number. The stability of the lower oxidation state becomes greater as you go down the group.

Key Term

Inert pair = ns^2 pair of electrons not involved in bonding.

Grade boost

You need examples to show octet expansion, e.g. NCl_3 is the only chloride of nitrogen, but phosphorus has two chlorides (PCl_3 and PCl_5) because it has access to *d*-orbitals to allow for octet expansion.

Pointer

Due to the inert pair effect the elements at the bottom of group 3 have a stable oxidation state of +1. The elements at the bottom of group 4 have a stable oxidation state of +2. Those at the bottom of group 5 have a +3 oxidation state.

Key Terms

Co-ordinate bond = shared pair of electrons, both from the same atom.

Dimer = a species created when two molecules join together.

Electron-deficient = a species with fewer than eight electrons in its outer shell, so this shell is not full.

Lone pair = pair of electrons in an outer shell that are not involved in bonding.

Grade boost

Read questions carefully – bonding and structure are different features and either can be asked. Any discussion of bonding in these molecules includes covalent and co-ordinate bonds and why they form. Structure includes areas such as bond angles and shapes – the $AlCl_3$ monomer is trigonal planar, but the structure becomes tetrahedral when the co-ordinate bond forms.

Group 3

Group 3 elements have three electrons in their outer shell, and these are arranged as ns^2np^1. The first two members of the group are boron and aluminium, and you only need to know about the chemistry of these two elements.

Electron deficiency

All group 3 elements have three outer electrons, and this allows them to form three covalent bonds to make compounds where they are electron-deficient. Common examples of **electron-deficient** group 3 compounds are BF_3, BCl_3 and $AlCl_3$. A lot of the chemistry of group 3 compounds is based around reactions with species with **lone pairs**, as this removes the electron deficiency by forming a **co-ordinate bond**.

Aluminium chloride

The aluminium atom in $AlCl_3$ is electron-deficient, and the chlorine atoms have three lone pairs each. This allows co-ordinate bonds to form between a chlorine atom of one $AlCl_3$ and the aluminium atom of another, with two co-ordinate bonds between $AlCl_3$ monomers forming a **dimer**.

Aluminium chloride can also form a co-ordinate bond with a chloride ion to form the tetrachloroaluminate ion, $AlCl_4^-$.

Structure of Aluminium chloride dimer

Bonding in Aluminium chloride dimer

Donor-acceptor compounds

The boron atom in BF_3 is electron-deficient, and like $AlCl_3$ it will try to react with molecules with lone pairs, such as NH_3, to get rid of the electron deficiency. These compounds are called donor-acceptor compounds because the NH_3 donates a lone pair to the bond that is made, and the BF_3 accepts it. Similar compounds can be formed from any electron-deficient group 3 compounds.

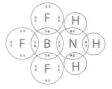

Structure of donor-acceptor compound (Structure of $NH_3.BF_3$)

Bonding in donor-acceptor compound (Bonding in $NH_3.BF_3$)

Boron nitride

Boron nitride, BN, is **isoelectronic** with carbon and so it forms similar structures to the allotropes of carbon: graphite, diamond and nanotubes.

Hexagonal boron nitride

This has a similar structure to graphite with layers of hexagons formed by covalent bonds between atoms. The main difference between them is that the hexagons in boron nitride have the atoms lying above one another with no delocalised electrons, whilst in graphite the atoms in adjacent layers do not lie above one another and there are delocalised electrons between the layers.

Both hexagonal boron nitride and graphite are soft because the forces between the layers are weak so the layers can slide over one another. Boron nitride differs from graphite as it is an insulator whilst graphite is an electrical conductor. Both materials can be used as lubricants, but the difference in electrical conductivity and relative inertness allows boron nitride to be used where graphite could not be.

Cubic boron nitride

This has a similar structure to diamond with a tetrahedral arrangement of boron atoms around nitrogen atoms and vice versa. It is one of the hardest materials known with a high melting temperature, and is an excellent heat conductor and chemically unreactive. These properties make it ideal for mounting high power electronic components, as wear-resistant coatings and as supports for catalysts.

Structure of boron nitride

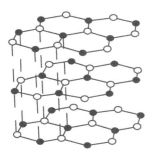

(a) Hexagonal boron nitride

Layers where nitrogen and boron atoms combined in a hexagonal network are superimposed and have a structure similar to graphite.

(b) Cubic boron nitride

Boron and nitrogen atoms combine three-dimensionally replacing carbon atoms in diamond.

Boron nitride nanotubes

A layer of hexagonal boron nitride can be used to wrap around carbon nanotubes. The boron nitride acts as an insulating layer around the conducting carbon nanotube to keep the current within the nanotube.

Key Term

Isoelectronic = same number of electrons in the outer shell.

Grade boost

Make sure you can recall the properties of graphite and boron nitride, and can link these to their structures.

Grade boost

Tin and lead show +2 and +4 oxidation states. In Tin +4 is the most stable, but in lead +2 is the most stable.

quickᴘιre

⑧ Carbon monoxide can be used as a reducing agent whilst PbO cannot. Explain this difference.

Group 4

In group 4, we study the differences between the elements, especially those at the top and bottom of the group. The differences are significant and are usually linked to the increase in metallic character down the group or the increasing stability of the +2 oxidation state.

Metal/non-metal properties

The elements at the top of group 4, carbon and silicon, are non-metals which have giant covalent structures. The two elements at the bottom of the group are tin and lead, and these are both metals so they have metallic bonding with lattices of positive metal ions in a sea of delocalised electrons.

Oxidation states

The maximum oxidation state in group 4 is +4, but the inert pair effect becomes more significant down the group, so the lower elements in the group have a +2 oxidation state as well.

Carbon is stable in an oxidation state of +4, and only exists as +2 in CO. This means that CO will act as a reducing agent as it tries to reach the stable +4 oxidation state. CO is used in the extraction of metals from their oxides, with the extraction of iron being the most common example:

$$Fe_2O_3 + 3\,CO \longrightarrow 2\,Fe + 3\,CO_2$$

Tin is also stable in the +4 oxidation state, so tin(II) compounds are reducing agents, such as in the reduction of nitrobenzene in unit 4.

Lead has compounds with both +4 and +2 oxidation states, such as PbO_2 and PbO. The +2 oxidation state is more stable, and so lead(IV) compounds are oxidising agents. An example of this is:

$$PbO_2\,(s) + 4\,HCl\,(conc.) \longrightarrow PbCl_2\,(s) + Cl_2\,(g) + 2\,H_2O\,(l)$$

Group 4 oxides and chlorides

At the top of group 4, the elements are non-metals, and so they use covalent bonding. In the case of CO_2, CCl_4 and $SiCl_4$ the compounds have simple molecular structures, with CO_2 being a gas and CCl_4 and $SiCl_4$ being liquids.

Lead(II) oxide and lead(II) chloride both use ionic bonding, and adopt giant ionic structures. These compounds are both solids.

Acid-base properties of oxides

Carbon dioxide is an **acidic oxide** so it reacts easily with bases.

$$2\ NaOH\ (aq) + CO_2\ (g) \longrightarrow Na_2CO_3\ (aq) + H_2O\ (l)$$

Like most p-block metal oxides, lead(II) oxide is an amphoteric oxide so it reacts with both acids and bases to form colourless solutions.

Reaction with an acid:

$$PbO\ (s) + 2\ HNO_3\ (aq) \longrightarrow Pb(NO_3)_2\ (aq) + H_2O\ (l)$$

Reaction with a base:

$$PbO\ (s) + 2\ NaOH\ (aq) + H_2O\ (l) \longrightarrow Na_2[Pb(OH)_4]\ (aq)$$

Reactions of chlorides with water

Most covalent chlorides react with water, so when $SiCl_4$ is added to water, the two liquids react very quickly, forming a white solid (SiO_2) and bubbles which release steamy fumes of HCl:

$$SiCl_4 + 2\ H_2O \longrightarrow SiO_2 + 4\ HCl$$

When CCl_4 is added to water it does not react, it forms a separate colourless liquid layer. This difference is due to the presence of d-orbitals in the outer shell of silicon, which are not present in carbon. These d-orbitals allow a lone pair from oxygen to bond to the silicon of the $SiCl_4$ to start the reaction. As carbon has no d-orbitals available, it cannot react.

Ionic chlorides like $PbCl_2$ do not react with water, and as $PbCl_2$ is insoluble it will remain as a white solid when mixed with water.

Reactions of Pb^{2+}

Most compounds of Pb^{2+} are insoluble, with lead(II) nitrate and lead(II) ethanoate being the only common soluble compounds. Adding other solutions to a solution containing Pb^{2+} (aq) ions usually causes a precipitate to form.

Ions added	Observation	Precipitate
OH^- (aq)	White precipitate	Lead(II) hydroxide, $Pb(OH)_2$
Excess OH^- (aq)	Precipitate dissolves to form colourless solution	Tetrahydroxoplumbate(II), $[Pb(OH)_4]^{2-}$ ions in solution
Cl^- (aq)	White precipitate	Lead(II) chloride, $PbCl_2$
I^- (aq)	Bright yellow precipitate	Lead(II) iodide , PbI_2

The precipitation reactions follow the same general ionic equation:

$$Pb^{2+}(aq) + 2\ X^-\ (aq) \longrightarrow MX_2\ (s)$$

Lead is an amphoteric metal, and so the white precipitate dissolves in excess sodium hydroxide solution according to the ionic equation:

$$Pb(OH)_2 + 2\ OH^- \longrightarrow [Pb(OH)_4]^{2-}$$

Key Terms

Acidic oxide = oxide that reacts with bases.

Basic oxide = oxide that reacts with acids.

Grade boost

Two metal ions form a yellow precipitate with iodide ions – silver and lead(II). This observation is regularly used in questions to identify these metals.

» Pointer

When discussing the lack of a reaction between water and CCl_4 it is important to realise that carbon has d-orbitals in the empty third and higher shells but has none in its outer (second) shell. These d-orbitals are not available as they are too high in energy.

quickfire

(9) Explain how sodium hydroxide solution can be used to distinguish between solutions of magnesium nitrate and lead(II) nitrate.

Key Term

Disproportionation = a reaction where atoms of the same element become oxidised and reduced to form two different products.

>> *Pointer*

When discussing oxidation and reduction, make sure you are clear and say iodide is a reducing agent, while iodine is an oxidising agent.

Group 7

You should be familiar with a lot of group 7 chemistry from your prior studies. This will include the physical appearance of the elements and the tests for chloride, bromide and iodide ions using silver nitrate.

Patterns in group 7 reactions

When studying the reactions of this group, the key factor is often the stability of different oxidation states. Standard electrode potentials, E^θ, are a measure of how good the elements are at oxidising other substances.

	E^θ / Volts
Cl_2 (aq) + 2e$^-$ $\rightleftharpoons$ 2 Cl$^-$(aq)	+1.36
Br_2 (aq) + 2e$^-$ $\rightleftharpoons$ 2 Br$^-$(aq)	+1.09
I_2 (aq) + 2e$^-$ $\rightleftharpoons$ 2 I$^-$(aq)	+0.54

Chlorine is the most oxidising, and iodine is the least oxidising of the three. This shows that the −1 oxidation state of chlorine is more stable than the −1 oxidation state of bromine or iodine.

Displacement reactions

During unit 1, you studied the displacement reactions of the halogens where a more reactive halogen oxidises the ions of a less reactive one, such as chlorine displacing bromide ions:

$$Cl_2 \text{ (g)} + 2 \text{ Br}^- \text{ (aq)} \longrightarrow 2 \text{ Cl}^- \text{ (aq)} + Br_2 \text{ (aq)}$$

In terms of standard electrode potentials (E^θ) we can show that because chlorine has a more positive E^θ than bromine, chlorine is a stronger oxidising agent and will oxidise bromide to bromine. You need to be able to explain the oxidation of iodide by chlorine or by bromine in a similar way.

Reaction of chlorine with sodium hydroxide

Chlorine reacts with dilute sodium hydroxide in one of two ways, depending on the temperature used. In the cold they make sodium chloride, NaCl, and sodium chlorate(I), NaOCl. This is a **disproportionation** reaction, with chlorine having a −1 oxidation state in NaCl and +1 in NaOCl:

$$Cl_2 + 2 \text{ NaOH} \longrightarrow \text{NaCl} + \text{NaOCl} + H_2O$$

When heated, a different reaction occurs to produce sodium chloride, NaCl, and sodium chlorate(V), $NaClO_3$. Once again this is a disproportionation reaction, with chlorine having a −1 oxidation state in NaCl and +5 in $NaClO_3$:

$$3 \, Cl_2 + 6 \text{ NaOH} \longrightarrow 5 \text{ NaCl} + NaClO_3 + 3 \, H_2O$$

Reaction of sodium halides with concentrated sulfuric acid

When you add concentrated sulfuric acid to any sodium halide, NaX, the same initial chemical reaction occurs, whether the halide is NaCl, NaBr or NaI. This reaction produces steamy fumes of HX gas:

$$NaX + H_2SO_4 \longrightarrow NaHSO_4 + HX$$

For NaCl, this is the only reaction that occurs, but HBr and HI react further because bromide and iodide have lower E^θ values, so it is easier to oxidise these halides.

HBr can be oxidised by the sulfuric acid to form Br_2 as orange fumes. During the process the sulfur in $NaHSO_4$ is reduced from +6, and forms SO_2 with an oxidation state of +4. The bromide is a strong enough reducing agent to reduce sulfur from +6 to +4.

HI can be oxidised by the sulfuric acid to form I_2 as a black solid or purple fumes. During the process the sulfur in $NaHSO_4$ is reduced from +6, and forms SO_2 with an oxidation state of +4, S as a yellow solid (oxidation state 0) and H_2S as a gas which smells of rotten eggs (oxidation state −2). The iodide is a much stronger reducing agent and can reduce sulfur from +6 to −2.

Uses of chlorine and chlorate (I)

- Both chlorine and chlorate (I) ions are oxidizing agents. They are more stable as the chloride ion, and their reduction from oxidation states of 0 (chlorine) or +1 (chlorate) to -1 in chloride is very favourable. This is the basis of many uses of both chlorine and chlorate (I).

$$Cl_2 + 2e \longrightarrow 2Cl^-$$
$$ClO^- + 2H^+ + 2e \longrightarrow Cl^- + H_2O$$

- Chlorine is used in the disinfection of water supplies. It kills bacteria by causing many of the essential biological molecules in them to be oxidised. When the DNA of the bacteria is oxidised it can no longer control the cell and the bacterium dies.
- Sodium chlorate(I), NaOCl contains ClO^- ions which kill bacteria and act as a bleach. This is because they are strong oxidising agents, and the oxidation of dyes forms colourless compounds. The oxidation of biological molecules by chlorate (I) has the same effect on microbes as the oxidation by chlorine, leading to its use as a bactericide.

>> *Pointer*

You need to recall the products and observations for the reactions of concentrated sulfuric acid with NaCl, NaBr and NaI and you must be able to link each observation with a specific compound.

Grade boost

When asked for a use of chlorine then a use of the element is needed. When asked for a use of a chlorine compound, then chlorine itself is not appropriate.

quicKpire

(10) List the sulfur-containing products of the reaction of NaI with concentrated sulfuric acid, giving the associated observation where possible.

Pointer

Transition elements are titanium to copper. Copper is a transition element because the Cu^{2+} ion has a partially filled *d*-orbital but zinc isn't because the atom and ions have full *d*-orbitals.

Grade boost

If you are asked to write electron arrangements for chromium or copper atoms, remember they are exceptions as they contain only one electron in their 4s orbitals, which gives a half-full or full set of *d*-orbitals.

Pointer

You need to recall the colours of many transition metal ions and oxoions that you have seen throughout the course. These include Cr^{3+} (dark green), CrO_4^{2-} (yellow), $Cr_2O_7^{2-}$ (orange), MnO_4^- (purple), Co^{2+} (pink), Fe^{2+} (pale green), Fe^{3+} (red-brown), Cu^{2+} (pale blue).

quickfire

⑪ Work out the electronic configurations of the atoms Ti and Co, and the ions Cr^{3+} and Ni^{2+}.

3.4 Chemistry of the *d*-block transition elements

d-block transition elements

The elements of the *d*-block are classed as **transition elements** if they have partially filled *d*-orbitals in their atoms or their ions. They share some key properties that you need to recall and explain:

- They have several different oxidation states.
- They form complexes by co-ordinate bonding, which are usually coloured.
- Both the metals themselves and their compounds can act as catalysts.

Electronic configurations

Electronic configurations show how the electrons are arranged in *s*, *p* and *d*-orbitals. The inner shells are full and contain 18 electrons, and these are arranged as $1s^2\,2s^22p^6\,3s^23p^6$. The outer electrons are in the 3*d* and 4*s* orbitals – remember that the 4*s* orbital is filled before the 3*d* orbitals.

Electronic configuration of vanadium — $3d^3$ $4s^2$

Electronic configuration of iron — $3d^6$ $4s^2$

Transition metal ions

When you write the electronic configuration for transition metals ions, remember that the atoms lose 4*s* electrons before the 3*d* electrons. This means the 4*s* orbital is empty in all the transition metal ions.

Electronic configuration of V^{3+} — $3d^2$ $4s^0$

Electronic configuration of Fe^{3+} — $3d^5$ $4s^0$

Oxidation states

The ionisation energies for electrons in *d*-orbitals are all similar, which causes each transition metal to have a variety of different oxidation states. You need to remember the common oxidation states of some common metals:

- Chromium: +3 and +6
- Manganese: +2, +4 and +7
- Iron: +2 and +3
- Cobalt: +2 and +3
- Copper: +1 and +2

Transition metal complexes

Complexes are made up of a transition metal ion bonded to atoms or molecules which surround it. There are empty orbitals on the metal ion and the ligands have lone pairs so they can form co-ordinate bonds together. The complexes usually have six **ligands** and an octahedral shape, although some have four ligands and a tetrahedral shape. Typical ligands include water (H_2O), ammonia (NH_3) and chloride (Cl^-).

Examples of complexes

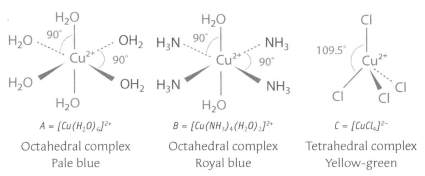

$A = [Cu(H_2O)_6]^{2+}$
Octahedral complex
Pale blue

$B = [Cu(NH_3)_4(H_2O)_2]^{2+}$
Octahedral complex
Royal blue

$C = [CuCl_4]^{2-}$
Tetrahedral complex
Yellow-green

If you dissolve a transition metal compound in water, the water molecules act as ligands and usually form octahedral complexes such as complex A. To turn complex A into one of the others, you need to add a solution that contains a new ligand – adding ammonia solution forms complex B, whilst adding concentrated hydrochloric acid forms complex C. Cobalt undergoes a similar ligand exchange with hydrochloric acid with the pink complex $[Co(H_2O)_6]^{2+}$ forming the blue tetrahedral complex $[CoCl_4]^{2-}$.

Colour of complexes

Transition metal ions are only coloured when they form complexes. In a transition metal ion, all the *d*-orbitals have the same energy level but when it forms a complex this causes the *d*-orbitals to split into two sets – 3 lower energy and 2 higher energy orbitals.

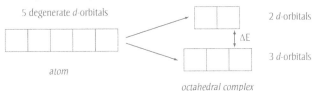

For electrons to move from the lower energy level to the higher energy they must absorb the correct amount of energy, ΔE. This energy corresponds to one specific frequency of light, as $\Delta E = hf$. The colour seen is made up of the frequencies of light which are not absorbed. Different ligands cause different splitting of the *d*-orbitals, so different frequencies are absorbed and this gives different colours.

Grade boost

When you draw the complexes, remember to use wedge and dotted lines to show the three-dimensional structure, with the bonds going to the atom with the lone pair.

≫ *Pointer*

Not all complexes are coloured. If a transition metal ion has filled *d*-orbitals (e.g. Cu^+) or empty *d*-orbitals (e.g. Sc^{3+}, Ti^{4+}) then electrons cannot move from the lower energy level to the higher one.

Grade boost

When you are describing the observations when sodium hydroxide is added to a solution, give the colour of the original solution and the colour of the precipitate. If the precipitate dissolves with excess sodium hydroxide, give the colour of the solution formed.

quickfire

⑫ Write ionic equations for the reactions with sodium hydroxide solution of Cu^{2+} and Fe^{3+}.

» Pointer

Copper(II) hydroxide is also formed when aqueous ammonia solution is added to copper(II) compounds in solution. It then reacts further to form a solution of the royal blue complex $[Cu(NH_3)_4(H_2O)_2]^{2+}$.

» Pointer

Make sure you can recall the listed examples of transition metal-based catalysts.

Reactions with sodium hydroxide

Many transition metal compounds form coloured solutions. If you add sodium hydroxide solution to these solutions, you will see a coloured precipitate. If you add even more sodium hydroxide until you have an excess, some precipitates can dissolve again to form a coloured solution.

	Colour of solution	Observation with NaOH (aq)	Observation with excess NaOH (aq)
Chromium(III), Cr^{3+}	green	grey-green precipitate	green solution
Iron(II), Fe^{2+}	pale green	dark green precipitate	no change
Iron(III), Fe^{3+}	yellow	red-brown precipitate	no change
Copper(II), Cu^{2+}	blue	pale blue precipitate	no change

These precipitation reactions follow one of two general ionic equations:

$$M^{2+}(aq) + 2\ OH^-\ (aq) \longrightarrow M(OH)_2\ (s)$$
$$M^{3+}(aq) + 3\ OH^-\ (aq) \longrightarrow M(OH)_3\ (s)$$

The reaction of excess sodium hydroxide with $Cr(OH)_3$ follows the equation:

$$Cr(OH)_3 + 3\ OH^- \longrightarrow [Cr(OH)_6]^{3-}$$

Uses of transition metals

Catalysts

Transition metal atoms and ions can act as catalysts for a range of reactions. Catalysts can be classified as heterogeneous or homogeneous:

Heterogeneous catalysts are those which are in a different physical state to the reactants. These include solid catalysts for gas phase or solution reactions. The reactants are adsorbed on the surface of the solid catalyst which brings them together.

Homogeneous catalysts are in the same physical state as the reactants. These have partially filled d-orbitals and variable oxidation states. This allows them to bond to reactant molecules and then oxidise or reduce these to make them far more reactive.

Some examples of transition metal catalysts are:

- Iron – Haber process for production of ammonia.
- Nickel – catalytic hydrogenation of alkenes.
- Vanadium(V) oxide – contact process for production of sulfuric acid.
- Manganese (IV) oxide – catalytic decomposition of hydrogen peroxide.

3.5 Chemical kinetics

Measuring and using reaction rates

Chemical kinetics is the study of the rates of chemical reactions and how they change. When measuring a reaction rate, we measure one factor as it changes over a period of time. Common methods of measuring rates are:

- Colourimetry – used when a coloured substance is created or used up during a chemical reaction.
- Measurement of gas volume (at constant pressure) with a gas syringe – used when a gas is produced in a chemical reaction.
- Measurement of mass – used when a gas is released in a chemical reaction.
- Measurement of gas pressure (at constant volume) – used for a reaction where reactants and products are gases and the number of gas molecules changes.
- Sampling and quenching – used when the methods above are not suitable. Small samples of the reaction mixture are removed at regular time intervals. To stop the reaction continuing the reaction is quenched, often by putting it into ice water to lower the temperature and reduce the reactant concentrations. Each sample can then be analysed by techniques such as titration.

Grade boost

If you are describing a method of measuring rates, then you must mention time to ensure you get your marks.

Pointer

These practical techniques can be assessed in either unit 3 or in unit 5.

Calculating rates

You can calculate rates from numerical values or graphs. If you are given values, then you need to divide the change in amount of substance or concentration by the time taken.

Time(s)	Concentration of reactant (mol dm^{-3})
0	1.50
60	1.20

$$Rate = \frac{change}{time} = \frac{(1.20 - 1.50)}{60} = -5.0 \times 10^{-3} \text{ mol dm}^{-3} \text{ s}^{-1}$$

If these are drawn as graphs, you need to draw a tangent to the curve and calculate its gradient in a similar manner to below.

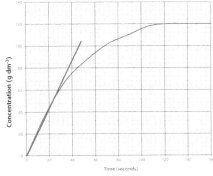

$$Rate = \frac{change}{time} = \frac{44}{20} = 2.2 \text{g dm}^{-3} \text{ s}^{-1}$$

Pointer

The units of rate depend on the units of the measurements given. Time is usually given in seconds, but if it is given in minutes then the rate would be, e.g. mol dm^{-3} min^{-1}.

quickfire

⑬ Give two methods of measuring the rate of the following reaction at 150°C:

$C_2H_4 (g) + Br_2(g) \rightarrow C_2H_4Br_2 (g)$

quickfire

⑭ In a reaction between sodium hydroxide and bromobutane, butanol is produced. If the reaction produces 0.046 moles of butanol in the first 10 seconds, calculate the initial rate giving its units.

Grade boost

Remember that the exam paper will include some questions that cover work from other A-level papers. In this topic, you could be asked to list the factors that affect rate and explain these in terms of frequency of successful collisions (collision theory).

Pointer

Orders of reaction can be given as numbers such as 0, 1 and 2 or described as being zeroth, first or second order.

quickfire

⑮ Give the order of the following reactions and the units of the rate constant in each case:
(a) Rate = k [HI] [Cl$_2$]
(b) Rate = k [O$_3$]

Orders of reaction

The rate of a chemical reaction will depend on the concentrations of the reactants, but this is not always a simple proportional relationship. When the concentration of one reactant (shown as [A]) is doubled, scientists have found that the rate of the reaction may be:

Unchanged	Rate is not dependent on concentration	rate α [A]^0
x 2	Rate is proportional to concentration	rate α [A]^1
x 4	Rate is proportional to concentration squared	rate α [A]^2

You can only work out the order from rate data, and not from the chemical equation. If you look at the table of data below, you can work out the order with respect to Br$_2$ and the order with respect to alkene.

	[Br$_2$] / mol dm^{-3}	[alkene] / mol dm^{-3}	Rate / mol dm^{-3} s^{-1}
1	1.0×10^{-3}	6.0×10^{-3}	0.5×10^{-3}
2	2.0×10^{-3}	6.0×10^{-3}	2.0×10^{-3}
3	6.0×10^{-3}	1.0×10^{-3}	3.0×10^{-3}
4	6.0×10^{-3}	2.0×10^{-3}	6.0×10^{-3}

We need to find two sets of data where only one concentration changes. In this case, we can use lines 1 and 2 where the concentration of Br$_2$ changes but the concentration of the alkene stays the same. As the concentration of Br$_2$ doubles, the rate increases by a factor of 4, which means that the reaction is second order with respect to Br$_2$.

Looking at lines 3 and 4, the concentration of the alkene changes but the concentration of Br$_2$ stays the same. As the concentration of alkene doubles, the rate increases by a factor of 2, which means that the reaction is first order with respect to alkene.

Rate equation

From this information, you can build up an overall rate equation. For the reaction above: rate = k [Br$_2$]^2[alkene]^1, k is called the rate constant.

2 is the order of the reaction with respect to Br$_2$, and 1 is the order of the reaction with respect to alkene. The overall order of the reaction is 3.

Rate constants

This is a constant in the rate equation. It is constant for a given reaction at a particular temperature, and is not affected by changing the concentrations, but changes if we change temperature or add a catalyst. The rate of a reaction in solution is typically quoted as mol dm^{-3} s^{-1}: This is the change in concentration (mol dm^{-3}) per second.

Order	Rate equation	Units of k
Zeroth	Rate = k	mol dm^{-3} s^{-1}
First	Rate = k [A]	s^{-1}
Second	Rate = k [A]^2	mol^{-1} dm^3 s^{-1}

Rates and mechanisms

The mechanism of a reaction is the series of steps that happen during a chemical reaction. The rate equation provides important information about one of these steps – this is the slowest step, which we call the **rate determining step**. The substances in the rate equation correspond to the reactants in the rate determining step and their orders correspond to the balancing numbers in the equation.

Examples

Rate = $k\,[N_2O_4]$ so the rate determining step must start $N_2O_4 \longrightarrow$

Rate = $k\,[NO]^2$ so the rate determining step must start $2\,NO \longrightarrow$

Rate = $k\,[H_2][I_2]$ so the rate determining step must start $H_2 + I_2 \longrightarrow$

If the rate determining step is $O_3 + Cl^- \longrightarrow O_2 + OCl^-$ then Rate = $k\,[O_3][Cl^-]$

Effect of temperature on rates

Increasing the temperature of a reaction causes the rate of a reaction to increase. In qualitative terms this is because the particles have more energy so more of the collisions have enough energy to cause a reaction ('activation energy').

In terms of the rate equation the reaction rate increases as the value of the rate constant, k, increases. We can quantify the effect of temperature on the rate constant using the Arrhenius equation.

$$k = Ae^{(-E_a/RT)}$$

k = Rate constant

A = Frequency factor. Its units are the same as the rate constant.

e = Mathematical constant, found on all scientific calculators.

E_a = Activation energy, used in J mol^{-1}. It is often given in kJ mol^{-1} which need to be multiplied by 1000.

R = Gas constant, given on the data sheet in units of J K^{-1} mol^{-1}. (8.31 J K^{-1} mol^{-1})

T = Temperature in Kelvin

The value of A gives the frequency of collisions, while the expression $e^{(-E_a/RT)}$ is a guide to the fraction of these that are successful. As the expression includes two constants (e, R) three out of the four remaining factors (k, A, E_a and T) must be known to calculate a value for the final factor. You can be asked to calculate any one of these variables.

Key Term

Rate determining step = the slowest step in a reaction mechanism.

quickfire

(16) a) Write a rate equation for a reaction that has the following rate determining step:

$N_2O_5 + H_2O \longrightarrow 2HNO_3$

b) Suggest a rate determining step for the alkaline hydrolysis of bromobutane which has the following rate equation:

Rate = $k\,[C_4H_9Br][OH^-]$

2 Rearrange the Arrhenius equation to give expressions for A =, E_a = and T =.

Grade boost

If you are not confident in rearranging the Arrhenius equation, then you will need to recall expressions for the rearranged equation.

quickfire

(17) A reaction has a rate constant of 1.76×10^3 s^{-1} at 298 K, and an activation energy of 66 kJ mol^{-1}. Calculate the value of the frequency factor, A, and hence calculate the rate constant at 308 K.

Pointer

The Arrhenius equation also explains the effects of catalysts. These reduce the activation energy so they increase the fraction of collisions that are successful.

3.6 Enthalpy changes for solids and solutions

Grade boost

Remember that the exam paper will include some questions that cover work from other A-level papers. In this topic, you could be asked to use Hess's law; enthalpy changes of combustion and formation and bond enthalpies.

Pointer

At A-level you can treat enthalpy as if it was exactly the same as energy.

Pointer

For a diatomic gas, such as Cl_2 or O_2 the enthalpy change of atomisation is equal to half the bond energy.

Grade boost

The solubility of a compound depends mainly on the enthalpy of solution being exothermic. The enthalpy of solution equals the lattice breaking enthalpy plus the enthalpy of hydration of the ions. This means the enthalpy of hydration for the ions must be greater than the enthalpy of lattice breaking for it to be soluble.

Enthalpy changes

Many enthalpy changes have special names, and you need to be familiar with these, although you will not have to give formal definitions.

Enthalpy change of atomisation: This is the enthalpy change to form one mole of atoms in the gas phase. For example:

$$Na\,(s) \longrightarrow Na\,(g) \quad \text{or} \quad \tfrac{1}{2}\,Cl_2\,(g) \longrightarrow Cl\,(g)$$

Enthalpy change of lattice formation: This is the enthalpy change that occurs when one mole of an ionic compound is formed from ions of the elements in the gas phase. For example:

$$Na^+\,(g) + Cl^-\,(g) \longrightarrow NaCl\,(s) \quad \text{or} \quad Ca^{2+}\,(g) + 2Cl^-\,(g) \longrightarrow CaCl_2\,(s)$$

Enthalpy change of lattice breaking: This is the reverse of lattice formation – it is the enthalpy change that occurs when one mole of an ionic compound is broken up into ions of the elements in the gas phase. For example:

$$NaCl\,(s) \longrightarrow Na^+\,(g) + Cl^-\,(g) \quad \text{or} \quad CaCl_2\,(s) \longrightarrow Ca^{2+}\,(g) + 2Cl^-\,(g)$$

Enthalpy change of hydration: This is the enthalpy change that occurs when one mole of gaseous ions is surrounded by water molecules to make a solution. For example:

$$Na^+\,(g) + aq \longrightarrow Na^+\,(aq) \quad \text{or} \quad Ca^{2+}\,(g) + aq \longrightarrow Ca^{2+}\,(aq)$$

Enthalpy change of solution: This is the enthalpy change that occurs when one mole of an ionic compound dissolves in water to form a solution. For example:

$$NaCl\,(s) + aq \longrightarrow NaCl\,(aq) \quad \text{or} \quad CaCl_2\,(s) + aq \longrightarrow CaCl_2\,(aq)$$

Relationship between enthalpy changes

You used Hess's law during a previous unit, and this states that when a change can occur by two different routes, the energy change for each is the same.

$$\Delta H = \Delta H_1 + \Delta H_2 + \Delta H_3$$

Formation of ionic compounds

The enthalpy change of formation for an ionic compound measures the enthalpy change when a compound is formed from its elements. We can build an energy cycle using the values for individual steps to calculate an unknown value in this process, usually the enthalpy of lattice formation as this cannot be measured directly.

To build an energy cycle to calculate the enthalpy of a change, write the equation that you wish to calculate and then produce an alternative route for the same change.

Example:

$$Na\ (s) + \tfrac{1}{2}\ Cl_2\ (g) \longrightarrow NaCl\ (s)$$

Equation	Enthalpy value / kJ mol^{-1}
$Na\ (g) \longrightarrow Na^+\ (g) + e^-$	496
$Cl\ (g) + e \longrightarrow Cl^-\ (g)$	−349
$Na\ (s) \longrightarrow Na\ (g)$	108
$Cl_2\ (g) \longrightarrow 2\ Cl\ (g)$	242
$Na^+\ (g) + Cl^-\ (g) \longrightarrow NaCl\ (s)$	−788

If we are to build a cycle based on the overall equation, then we must find equations in the table that contain the same substances as we have in the overall equation.

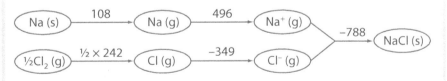

We see that we now need to connect the Na with the Na$^+$ and the Cl with the Cl$^-$.

This creates a complete cycle, and we can calculate the overall value by starting at the Na (s) + ½ Cl$_2$ (g) and then following the cycle around to the NaCl (s).

$$\Delta H = 108 + (½ \times 242) + 496 - 349 - 788 = -412 \text{ kJ mol}^{-1}$$

Stability of compounds

One way of judging if a compound is stable is to use the enthalpy of formation. In general, a compound is stable relative to the elements if the enthalpy of formation is negative (exothermic). The more negative the value, the more stable the compound.

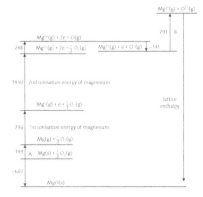

3.7 Entropy and feasibility of reactions

>> Pointer

Take care with using S and ΔS. The entropy of a gas would be S (gas) while ΔS refers to the entropy change during a chemical reaction or physical change.

Grade boost

A common error is to use the incorrect units in calculating ΔG. The entropy must be divided by 1000 to convert J into kJ, and the temperature must be given in Kelvin.

quickfire

(18) Calculate the entropy change for the reaction below:

$Na_2CO_3(s) \longrightarrow$
$Na_2O(s) + CO_2(g)$

	Entropy, S/ $J\ K^{-1}\ mol^{-1}$
Na_2CO_3 (s)	136
Na_2O (s)	73
CO_2 (g)	214

quickfire

(19) Calculate the enthalpy change for the reaction above using the enthalpies of formation below.

	$\Delta_f H$ / kJ mol^{-1}
Na_2CO_3 (s)	−1131
Na_2O (s)	−416
CO_2 (g)	−394

Entropy

Entropy is a quantity which measures the freedom of molecules, or atoms within a molecule. Where molecules have greater freedom, this leads to greater disorder. In any natural change, overall entropy will tend to increase.

The molecules in gases have more freedom than those in liquids, with the freedom of molecules in solids being the least. This means that the entropy of a gas will be greatest, followed by liquids, with solids having the lowest entropy. We can write this as:

$$S \text{ (gas)} > S \text{ (liquid)} > S \text{ (solid)}$$

Unlike enthalpy terms, entropy values and entropy changes are given in $J\ K^{-1}\ mol^{-1}$. To calculate the entropy change during a chemical reaction, you can use the entropy of each of the reactants and products. For the formation of water from its elements:

$$H_2 \text{ (g)} + \tfrac{1}{2} O_2 \text{ (g)} \longrightarrow H_2O \text{ (l)}$$
$$\Delta S = S(H_2O(l)) - S(H_2(g)) - \tfrac{1}{2}S(O_2(g)) = 70 - 131 - \tfrac{1}{2} \times 205$$
$$= -163.5\ J\ K^{-1}\ mol^{-1}$$

Gibbs free energy

The reaction of hydrogen and oxygen gases to give water has a negative entropy change, but as entropy always tends to increase in natural changes you may think this means the reaction will not happen. The reality is that the reaction between hydrogen and oxygen is very feasible. This is because an exothermic reaction increases the entropy of the surroundings, and we need to factor this into the calculations. The value which combines enthalpy and entropy is the Gibbs free energy, ΔG:

$$\Delta G = \Delta H - T \Delta S$$

If the value of ΔG is negative, the reaction can occur spontaneously.

If the value of ΔG is positive, the reaction cannot occur spontaneously.

This balance between enthalpy and entropy will allow endothermic processes to occur such as boiling, dissolving sodium chloride or thermal decomposition reactions. In each case the greater freedom of the particles in the liquid solution or gas phase causes a significant increase in entropy in the change, and this is greater than the enthalpy change, especially at higher temperatures making the overall value negative.

Using Gibbs free energy

The Gibbs free energy can be used to find out the temperature required for a reaction to occur. As the temperature changes, the value of the Gibbs free energy changes with it due to the inclusion of temperature in the expression:

$$\Delta G = \Delta H - T\Delta S$$

The value of the Gibbs free energy needs to be negative for a reaction to occur, and at the temperature that the reaction just begins to be possible, the value of the Gibbs free energy must just become negative. At this point $\Delta G = 0$, and so you can write:

$$\Delta H - T\Delta S = 0 \qquad \text{so} \qquad T = \Delta H \div \Delta S$$

ΔH and ΔS need the same energy units, but are usually given in different ones, so the first step is to multiply ΔH by 1000 to convert it into J mol^{-1}. The calculation produces a temperature in K.

Example

Calcium carbonate decomposes when heated to form calcium oxide and carbon dioxide:

$$CaCO_3\ (s) \longrightarrow CaO\ (s) + CO_2\ (g)$$

For this reaction $\Delta H = 178$ kJ mol^{-1} and $\Delta S = 161$ J K^{-1} mol^{-1}. Use these values to find the minimum temperature needed for the decomposition to occur.

Answer

At the minimum temperature for the reaction, $\Delta G = 0$ and from this we can show that: $T = \Delta H \div \Delta S$ so that $T = 178{,}000 \div 161 = 1106$ K.

Grade boost

You must state the units whenever you calculate a temperature, as the answer could be in Kelvin or °C. To convert between these units, subtract 273 from the temperature in Kelvin to get the value in °C.

quickfire

(20) Use the answers to Quickfire questions 18 and 19 to calculate the Gibbs free energy change for this reaction at 300 K.

quickfire

(21) Use the answers to Quickfire questions 18 and 19 to calculate the minimum temperature for the reaction to occur.

3.8 Equilibrium constants

General equilibria

An equilibrium is set up when a reversible reaction reaches a point where the amounts of reactants and products stay the same because the rates of the forward and reverse reactions are equal. In unit 1 you studied how these amounts changed when temperature and pressure changed, using Le Chatelier's principle. This method does not allow you to work out the amounts of each reactant and product, and to do this you need to use an equilibrium constant.

Writing equilibrium constants

There are two types of general equilibrium constant K_c and K_p. K_c is the equilibrium constant in terms of concentration. It is used for solutions, but can also be used for other types of mixture if you are given concentrations. For a reversible reaction in solution of the type:

$$a\,A\,(aq) + b\,B\,(aq) \rightleftharpoons x\,X\,(aq) + y\,Y\,(aq)$$

The equilibrium constant for the reaction in solution is:

$$K_c = \frac{[X]^x[Y]^y}{[A]^a[B]^b} \text{ where } [X] \text{ represents the concentration of X}$$

The top line has the concentrations of all the products to the powers of the balancing numbers, multiplied together. The bottom line has the concentrations of all the reactants to the powers of the balancing number, multiplied together. For example:

For the reaction: $Sn^{4+} + 2\,Fe^{2+} \rightleftharpoons 2\,Fe^{3+} + Sn^{2+}$

The equilibrium constant, K_c, is given by: $K_c = \dfrac{[Fe^{3+}]^2\,[Sn^{2+}]}{[Sn^{4+}]\,[Fe^{2+}]^2}$

K_p is the equilibrium constant in terms of partial pressures and it is only useful for gas mixtures. We write the expression for the equilibrium constant K_p in a similar way to K_c. For the reversible reaction between gases shown:

$$a\,A\,(g) + b\,B\,(g) \rightleftharpoons x\,X\,(g) + y\,Y\,(g)$$

The equilibrium constant for the reaction is:

$$K_p = \frac{p_X^x\,p_Y^y}{p_A^a\,p_B^b} \text{ where } p_X \text{ represents the partial pressure of X}$$

The top line has the partial pressures of all the products to the powers of their balancing numbers, multiplied together. The bottom line has the partial pressures of all the reactants to the powers of their balancing numbers, multiplied together. For example:

For the reaction: $N_2O_4\,(g) \rightleftharpoons 2\,NO_2\,(g)$

The equilibrium constant, K_p is given by: $K_p = \dfrac{p_{NO_2}^2}{p_{N_2O_4}}$

Calculating K_p or K_c

You can calculate the values of K_c and K_p if you are given information about the concentrations of reactants and products at equilibrium (for K_c) or the partial pressures of these (for K_p). In a relatively straightforward example, you would be given all the concentrations that you need.

Example: In a mixture of hydrogen and iodine vapours, the following reversible reaction occurs: $H_2 + I_2 \rightleftharpoons 2\ HI$

The equilibrium mixture produced during this reaction contains 0.0035 mol dm^{-3} of each reactant and 0.0235 mol dm^{-3} HI. Calculate the value of K_c.

Answer: $\dfrac{[HI]^2}{[H_2][I_2]} = \dfrac{0.0235^2}{0.0035 \times 0.0035} = 45.1$

Because there are two concentrations on the top line of the expression and two on the bottom, they cancel out and K_c **has no units**.

> **Pointer**
>
> Some equilibrium constants have units and some do not. If there are the same numbers of concentration terms on the top and bottom lines of the equilibrium constant, then these units cancel out and there are no units. If there are different numbers of concentration terms on the top and bottom lines of the equilibrium constant then some units cancel out, but some units remain behind.
> $$\frac{\text{mol dm}^{-3} \times \cancel{\text{mol dm}^{-3}}}{\cancel{\text{mol dm}^{-3}}}$$

Working out equilibrium mixtures

If the information given does not list the concentrations of every reactant and product at equilibrium, then you need to work these out. A common example is when you are given the concentrations of each reactant at the start and then given the concentration of **one** product at equilibrium.

Example: If an equimolar solution of A and B where the concentration of each is 0.5 mol dm^{-3} is allowed to reach equilibrium then the equilibrium mixture contains 0.2 mol dm^{-3} of D. Calculate the value of K_c.

$$A + B \longrightarrow 2\ C + D$$

Answer:

	[A]	[B]	[C]	[D]
Concentrations at the start / mol dm^{-3}	0.5	0.5	0	0
Concentrations at equilibrium / mol dm^{-3}	0.3	0.3	0.4	0.2

At the start, we only have A and B, both with concentration 0.5 mol dm^{-3}.

At equilibrium, we have [D] = 0.2 mol dm^{-3}, but since 2 C are made when each D is made then [C] = 0.4 mol dm^{-3}.

To make 0.2 D we must use up 0.2 A and 0.2 B, leaving 0.3 of each behind.

We must now write an expression for K_c and put these values into it to get the value of K_c. Remember to include the units.

So the equilibrium constant is: $K_c = \dfrac{[C]^2[D]}{[A][B]} = \dfrac{0.4^2 \times 0.2}{0.3 \times 0.3} = 0.355$ mol dm^{-3}

What do equilibrium constants tell us?

Equilibrium constants can give us a guide to the degree that an equilibrium lies towards products or starting materials. An equilibrium that has similar amounts of starting materials and products would have a K_c value around 1.

If K_c is a lot less than 1, then very little of the products are formed, and most of the mixture is starting materials. This is the case when ΔG is positive, as the reaction doesn't occur spontaneously.

If K_c is a lot more than 1, then most of the reactants have been converted into products. This is the case when ΔG for the reaction is negative, as the reaction will occur spontaneously.

> **Pointer**
> When an equilibrium is described as exothermic, this means it is exothermic as it is written. The forward reaction is exothermic and the reverse reaction will be endothermic.

Effect of conditions on K_c and K_p

The name 'equilibrium constant' suggests that the values of K_c and K_p would always be the same, and this is generally true. The only factor that will change the value of K_c or K_p is temperature – if we change pressure, add a catalyst or make any other changes, the values of K_c and K_p stay the same. When we change the temperature, we must use Le Chatelier's principle to work out the effect on the equilibrium position.

If the reaction is exothermic, increasing the temperature will shift the equilibrium to the left as this is the endothermic direction. This decreases the products (the top line of the equilibrium constant) and increases the reactants (the bottom line of the equilibrium constant) which makes the equilibrium constant smaller.

If the reaction is endothermic, increasing the temperature will shift the equilibrium to the right as this is the endothermic direction. This increases the products (the top line of the equilibrium constant) and decreases the reactants (the bottom line of the equilibrium constant) which makes the equilibrium constant larger.

Example

$$N_2 + 3H_2 \rightleftharpoons 2NH_3 \quad \textit{Exothermic}$$

If the temperature is increased, the equilibrium will shift to the endothermic direction, which is to the left, to counteract the temperature change. This increases the concentration of N_2 and H_2 and decreases the concentration of NH_3. The equilibrium constant, K_c is:

$$K_c = \frac{[NH_3]^2}{[N_2][H_2]^3}$$

The effect on this change is to decrease $[NH_3]$ and increase $[N_2]$ and $[H_2]$ which will decrease the value of K_c.

quickfire

㉓ Explain the effect of increasing temperature on the equilibrium constant, K_p, for the exothermic reaction below.

$$2SO_2(g) + O_2(g) \rightleftharpoons 2SO_3(g)$$

Equilibria and rates

Equilibrium and kinetic data can both give us information about chemical reactions; however, they tell us different things:

Equilibrium data tells us about the relative stability of the reactants and products, and the energy changes that occur. It tells us nothing about how the reaction occurs.

Reaction rates give us information about the changes that occur between the reactants and transition state. This allows us to deduce what is happening *during* the reaction, giving the **reaction mechanism**.

Applying equilibrium and rate equations

Companies consider kinetic, energetic and equilibrium data when planning any process and any industrial reaction aims to produce the maximum amount of product as quickly as possible using the least energy. Often a compromise is needed which gets each of these as close to each ideal value as possible.

Equilibrium: The equilibrium yield of product can be changed by altering concentration, pressure or temperature. The equilibrium constant tells us which concentration or pressure values favour high yield, and the energetics shows us whether the reaction is exothermic or endothermic.

Rates: The rates can be made as fast as possible by increasing temperature, increasing pressure or adding a catalyst.

Energetics: Energy calculations will identify how much energy needs to be input into the system for a reaction to occur, avoiding the input of excess energy. Similarly, if a reaction is exothermic, we may harness the energy released rather than just lose it as waste heat.

>> *Pointer*

You should be prepared to interpret data on different conditions or routes to form a compound. In addition to rates of reaction and yield of products, you should consider aspects of green chemistry. These include the atom economy, whether the starting materials are sustainable and whether any of the side products are harmful.

Key Terms

Acid = H^+ ion donor
(a proton donor).

Base = H^+ ion acceptor
(a proton acceptor).

>> *Pointer*

You will see the term proton used interchangeably with H^+, because a hydrogen ion is just a single proton.

Grade boost

Don't confuse strong acids with concentrated acids. Strong and weak refer to how many of the molecules release H^+ ions, while concentrated and dilute refers to how much acid has been dissolved in a volume of water.

(24) Calculate the pH of a solution where $[H^+]$ is 0.015 mol dm^{-3}.

>> *Pointer*

To calculate 10^{-pH} on many calculators you use the INV or SHIFT button before pressing $\log_{10}$.

quickfire

(25) Calculate the concentration of H^+ in a solution with a pH of 3.2.

3.9 Acid-base equilibria

Acids and bases

In your earlier work, you will have seen that Lowry and Brönsted defined **acids** and **bases** in terms of winning and losing H^+ ions and that acids can be classified as strong or weak.

Strong acids donate all their H^+ ions in aqueous solution, for example hydrochloric acid:

$$HCl\ (aq) + H_2O\ (l) \longrightarrow H_3O^+\ (aq) + Cl^-\ (aq)$$

Weak acids donate some of their H^+ ions in aqueous solution because they set up a dynamic equilibrium, for example ethanoic acid:

$$CH_3COOH\ (aq) + H_2O\ (l) \rightleftharpoons CH_3COO^-\ (aq) + H_3O^+\ (aq)$$

In both these equations H_2O is accepting a proton and so it is acting as a base, but this is not the only base in each equation. Because the second equation is an equilibrium we can write the equation in either direction, and in the reverse reaction CH_3COO^- accepts a H^+ ion from H_3O^+ – the CH_3COO^- is acting as a base. We call the CH_3COO^- the conjugate base of CH_3COOH, and H_3O^+ is the conjugate acid of H_2O.

pH and acidity

The acidity of acids is usually quoted on the pH scale. This commonly ranges from 0 (strong acid) through 7 (neutral) to 14 (strong alkali).

0	1	2	3	4	5	6	7	8	9	10	11	12	13	14
Strong Acid			**Weak Acid**			**Neutral**		**Weak Alkali**			**Strong Alkali**			

Acids have pH values below 7.   *Alkalis have pH values above 7.*

The further a 1 mol dm^{-3} solution's pH value is below neutral (7), the stronger the acid.

The further a 1 mol dm^{-3} solution's pH value is above neutral (7), the stronger the alkali.

The numbers on the pH scale are calculated from the concentration of H^+(aq) ions in the solution. pH is defined as:

$$pH = -\log_{10}[H^+(aq)]$$

So for a H^+ concentration of 0.15 mol dm^{-3}, pH = $-\log(0.15)$ = 0.82.

You can also use this formula to work out the concentration of H^+ in a solution where you know the pH. The rearranged formula is:

$$[H^+(aq)] = 10^{-pH}$$

Since pH is a log scale, one unit is equivalent to a 10 times change in H^+ concentration, so 2 pH units are 100 times and 3 represent 1000 times.

Equilibrium constants for acids

The dissociation of an acid is an equilibrium process so it has an equilibrium constant. The equilibrium is:

$$HA \ (aq) \ \rightleftharpoons \ H^+(aq) + A^-\ (aq)$$

This equilibrium is simplified because it ignores the involvement of water and it has a special equilibrium constant called K_a. For the acid HA:

$$K_a = \frac{[H^+][A^-]}{[HA]}$$

The more dissociated the acid is, the more hydrogen ions and anions there will be, so the larger the value of K_a. A weak acid has a low value of K_a and a strong acid has a high value of K_a.

Calculating pH for strong and weak acids

To calculate the pH of an acid we need to know the concentration of H^+ ions in the solution. We calculate $[H^+]$ in different ways for strong acids and weak acids.

Strong acids

For a strong monobasic acid, all the molecules of the acid release H^+ ions so $[H^+]$ equals the concentration of the strong acid. For example, 0.10 mol dm^{-3} HCl solution would have $[H^+] = 0.10$ mol dm^{-3}.

$$pH = -\log_{10}[H^+(aq)] = -\log_{10}(0.10) \quad so \quad pH = 1$$

Weak acids

For a weak acid, not all the molecules of the acid release H^+ ions so the concentration of the H^+ in solution will be less than the concentration of the acid, and will vary from acid to acid. To work out $[H^+]$ we need to know the value of K_a for the acid. For ethanoic acid, $K_a = 1.7 \times 10^{-5}$ mol dm^{-3}, so to find $[H^+]$ in a 1.0 mol dm^{-3} solution we see that:

$$K_a = \frac{[H^+][CH_3COO^-]}{[CH_3COOH]}$$

Since each CH_3COOH molecule that dissociates produces one CH_3COO^- and one H^+, then $[H^+] = [CH_3COOH]$ giving:

$$K_a = \frac{[H^+]^2}{[CH_3COO^-]}$$

For a weak acid, very few of the molecules have dissociated so we can assume that the concentration of CH_3COOH present is the same as the concentration we put in. In this case this gives:

$$K_a = \frac{[H^+]^2}{[CH_3COOH]} \quad \text{which rearranges to give } [H^+] = \sqrt[2]{K_a \times [CH_3COOH]}$$

In this example $\quad [H^+] = \sqrt[2]{1.7 \times 10^{-5} \times 1.0} = 4.1 \times 10^{-3}$ mol dm^{-3}

Using $\qquad\qquad pH = -\log [H^+] = -\log (4.1 \times 10^{-3}) = \textbf{pH = 2.4}$

≫ **Pointer**

Because all K_a expressions are similar, with two concentrations on the top and one on the bottom, the units are always the same: mol dm^{-3}.

quickfire

㉖ Work out the pH of a solution of a 0.5 mol dm^{-3} methanoic acid, HCOOH ($K_a = 1.6 \times 10^{-5}$ mol dm^{-3}).

quickfire

㉗ A 0.5 mol dm^{-3} solution of a monobasic acid has a pH of 4.5. Calculate the value of K_a for this acid.

≫ Pointer

Because the expression for K_w is always the same, with two concentrations multiplied together the units are always the same: $mol^2\ dm^{-6}$.

≫ Pointer

You need to be able to write expressions and units for K_a and K_w. You do not need to recall values for K_a or K_w.

quickfire

28 Work out the pH of a solution of a 0.3 mol dm^{-3} solution of the strong base, NaOH.

Dissociation of water

Although we always write water as H_2O, any sample of pure water will always include a very small amount of H^+ and OH^- ions. This is due to a reversible reaction which is present in all samples of water:

$$H_2O\ (l) \rightleftharpoons H^+(aq) + OH^-\ (aq)$$

The equilibrium lies mainly to the left-hand side, so almost all the water exists as water molecules, with a very small amount of ions. Because the concentration of water stays effectively constant, we can write an equilibrium constant called the *ionic product of water*, K_w.

$$K_w = [H^+][OH^-]$$

The value of K_w is constant at a particular temperature, and at 25 °C the value of K_w is approximately $1.0 \times 10^{-14}\ mol^2\ dm^{-6}$.

When an acid reacts with a base, the reaction is the reverse of the equilibrium above and the equation for the neutralisation reaction is:

$$H^+\ (aq) + OH^-\ (aq) \longrightarrow H_2O\ (l)$$

Calculating pH for strong bases

To calculate the pH of any solution we need to know the concentration of H^+ ions in the solution. Even in a solution of a base there will be free H^+ ions, but there will be fewer than are present in water. To find the $[H^+]$ we need to use the expression for K_w:

$$K_w = [H^+][OH^-] \text{ so } [H^+] = \frac{K_w}{[OH^-]}$$

For a strong base, all the hydroxide ions will be dissociated from the base so $[OH^-]$ will equal the concentration of the base. For a solution of NaOH of concentration 0.2 mol dm^{-3}, with $K_w = 1.0 \times 10^{-14}\ mol^2\ dm^{-6}$ then:

$$[H^+] = \frac{K_w}{[OH^-]} = \frac{1.0 \times 10^{-14}}{0.2} = 5 \times 10^{-14}\ mol\ dm^{-3}$$

Using our expression for pH $= -\log_{10}[H^+] = -\log_{10}(5 \times 10^{-14}) = 13.3$

Buffers

Buffers are solutions whose pH stays relatively constant as a small amount of an acid or alkali is added. The buffer solution maintains a nearly constant pH by removing any added H^+ or OH^-. Typically, a buffer solution is made from a mixture of a weak acid and a salt from the same acid, e.g. CH_3COOH and CH_3COONa. They are used to keep the pH constant when enzymes are stored or used.

Grade boost

When writing the two equations for explaining buffers, you must identify that one is reversible and the other is not.

How do buffers work?

In a buffer solution, the salt dissociates completely:

$$CH_3COONa \ (aq) \longrightarrow CH_3COO^- \ (aq) + Na^+ \ (aq)$$

The acid dissociates partly in a reversible reaction:

$$CH_3COOH \ (aq) \rightleftharpoons H^+(aq) + CH_3COO^-(aq)$$

According to Le Chatelier's principle, the high concentration of CH_3COO^- released by the salt will force this equilibrium to the left, meaning that very little of the acid will dissociate.

When an acid is added to a buffer, this increases the concentration of H^+ so the reversible reaction will shift to the left, removing the H^+ ions by reaction with CH_3COO^-.

When a base is added to a buffer, this reacts with H^+ ions and decreases their concentration so the reversible reaction will shift to the right, releasing more H^+ ions from the CH_3COOH.

A similar buffer system for maintaining alkaline pH is based on a mixture of ammonium chloride and ammonia solution. In this case the equilibrium which shifts upon addition of acid or base is:

$$NH_4^+ \rightleftharpoons NH_3 + H^+$$

Pointer

When a buffer has equal concentrations of the acid and salt then $[H^+] = K_a$ for the acid.

pH of buffers

To calculate the pH of a buffer solution you need to assume that all the salt dissociates so $[CH_3COO^-] = [CH_3COONa]$, and none of the acid does so $[CH_3COOH]$ equals the concentration of acid used.

$$K_a = \frac{[H^+][CH_3COO^-]}{[CH_3COOH]} \quad \text{so} \quad [H^+] = \frac{K_a \times [CH_3COOH]}{[CH_3COO^-]}$$

If we make a buffer from 0.20 mol dm^{-3} CH_3COOH and 0.20 mol dm^{-3} CH_3COONa (K_a for $CH_3COOH = 1.7 \times 10^{-5}$ mol dm^{-3}) to calculate the pH we need to calculate $[H^+]$ then use the equation for pH.

$$[H^+] = \frac{1.7 \times 10^{-5} \times (0.20)}{(0.20)} = 1.7 \times 10^{-5} \text{ mol dm}^{-3}$$

$$pH = -\log_{10}[H^+] = -\log_{10}(1.7 \times 10^{-5}) = 4.8$$

quickfire

(29) Calculate the pH of a buffer solution that contains 0.10 mol dm^{-3} HCOOH and 0.20 mol dm^{-3} HCOONa. (K_a for HCOOH = 1.6×10^{-5} mol dm^{-3}.)

Acid-base titrations

When an alkali is added to an acid, a neutralisation reaction occurs. This leads to an increase in the pH as the alkali is added; however, the change does not form a straight-line graph. The shape of the graph depends on whether the acid and base are strong or weak.

Strong acid-strong base titration curve (HCl with NaOH)

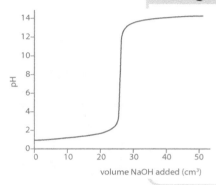

volume NaOH added (cm³)

The pH increases slowly until the amount of NaOH added approaches the amount of HCl, when there is a sudden increase. The middle region of the curve is vertical, before it levels off at the end. The midpoint of the vertical region is called the equivalence point, and here the amount of alkali added equals the amount of acid.

Titration curve for addition of 0.1 mol dm⁻³ NaOH to 25cm³ 0.1 mol dm⁻³ HCl

Indicators

We can identify the equivalence point using an indicator. An indicator is a weak acid or base, where the dissociated and undissociated molecules are different colours.

methyl orange (red form)
(in acid)

methyl orange (orange form)
(in alkali)

The indicator changes colour over a small range of pH, but as long as this range lies within the vertical part of the curve then the colour change occurs when only a single drop of the basic solution is added. Different indicators change over different pH ranges, and the values for some indicators are given in the table.

Indicator	Approximate colour change range
Phenolphthalein	8.3 − 10.0
Bromothymol blue	6.0 − 7.5
Litmus	4.0 − 6.5
Methyl orange	3.2 − 4.4

Titration curves including weak acids or weak bases

When a weak acid is used in a titration, the vertical region in the titration curve is shorter, and the curve starts at a higher pH due to the weaker acid. The curve increases more gradually towards the equivalence point, but has a plateau at about half the volume needed for neutralisation. The plateau is due to the formation of a mixture of a salt and acid at this point, and this causes a buffer effect.

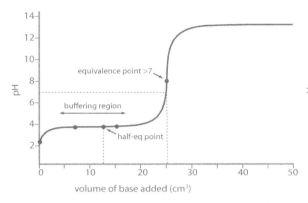

Titration curve for addition of 0.1 mol dm⁻³ NaOH to 0.1 mol dm⁻³ CH₃COOH.

Titration curve for addition of 0.1 mol dm⁻³ NH₃ to 0.1 mol dm⁻³ HCl.

The strong acid/weak base curve shows a similar pattern in the basic region of the graph, with a gradual increase from pH 7 until it reaches a plateau (buffer effect) and after this it increases gradually to its final pH which will be lower than 14 as the base is weak. The weak acid/weak base titration curve does not have a vertical region so it is not suitable for titration with an indicator and a pH probe must be used.

pH of salts

At the equivalence point of each of these curves, we have a solution of the salt formed from the acid and base. The pH of this solution is the mid-point of the vertical part of the curve, and for a strong acid/strong base it is 7 showing that the solution of the salt in this case is neutral. When we have a weak acid and a strong base, the salt formed is not neutral, and it forms a solution that is basic, with a pH of around 8–10. This is because the salt releases all its anions, such as the ethanoate anion, CH_3COO^-, and these react and remove H^+ ions from solution due to the equilibrium below:

$$H^+(aq) + CH_3COO^-(aq) \rightleftharpoons CH_3COOH (aq)$$

When we have a strong acid and a weak base, the salt formed is acidic, with a pH of around 4–6. This is because the cation present, e.g. NH_4^+, can dissociate to release H^+ ions in a reversible reaction:

$$NH_4^+ \rightleftharpoons NH_3 + H^+$$

Grade boost

In a weak acid/strong base titration an equimolar mixture of acid and salt is formed when half the volume of base needed for neutralisation is added. This is a buffer and has pH = −log K_a.

Pointer

Since the indicator used in a titration must change colour completely in the vertical region of the curve, not every indicator will work for these titrations. Using the table on the last page we see that phenolphthalein is best for a strong base/weak acid and methyl orange is best for weak base/strong acid.

Summary: UNIT 3 Physical and Inorganic Chemistry

3.1 Redox and standard electrode potentials

Redox

- Any redox reaction has one species being reduced and one being oxidised.
- Oxidation and reduction can be defined using:
  - Electron transfer (oxidation is loss of electrons, reduction is gain of electrons).
  - Oxidation states (during oxidation, oxidation states become more positive, and during reduction they become less positive).
- Fuel cells can be used to obtain energy from fuels.
  - Advantages include high efficiency and no greenhouse gas emissions produced from hydrogen gas.
  - Disadvantages include the use of fossil fuels to produce hydrogen and difficulty of storing flammable hydrogen gas.

Electrochemistry

- Electrochemical cells are made up of two half-cells joined by a salt bridge and high-resistance voltmeter.
- A standard electrode potential is measured by connecting a half-cell to the standard hydrogen electrode.
- Standard conditions are 1 atm pressure, 1 mol dm^{-3} concentration and a temperature of 298 K.
- The EMF of a cell is the difference between the standard electrode potentials of the two half-cells.
- A reaction is feasible if the EMF is positive.

3.2 Redox Reactions

- Redox reactions can be formed by combining two half-equations – one for an oxidation and one for a reduction.
- Redox titrations give information on concentrations of solutions, using the equation moles = concentration (in mol dm^{-3}) × volume (in dm^3).
- Copper ions can be studied by titration by adding iodide ions, which releases iodine (I_2).

3.3 *p*-block chemistry

- Many compounds are amphoteric – they react with both acids and alkalis.
- They can have different oxidation states due to:
  - The inert pair effect – this lowers the oxidation state by 2 and becomes more important down the group.
  - Octet expansion – this allows elements in the third period and below to have oxidation states above +4 by using *d*-orbitals.

Group 3

- Many compounds are electron deficient – the atoms have fewer than 8 electrons in their outer shell.
- They form co-ordinate bonds with lone pairs, which form dimers such as Al_2Cl_6.
- Boron nitride has a similar structure and bonding to graphite, but it doesn't conduct as the electrons are localised.

Group 4

- They change from non-metals to metals down the group.
- They are stable in the +4 oxidation state, apart from lead which is stable as +2.
- The oxides are acidic at the top of the group, becoming amphoteric at the bottom.
- CCl_4 doesn't react with water, but $SiCl_4$ does.
- Lead(II) compounds are insoluble, apart from $Pb(NO_3)_2$ and $(CH_3COO)_2Pb$.

Group 7

- The elements become weaker oxidising agents down the group.
- The halogens that are stronger oxidising agents can displace the lower halide ions from solution.
- Cl_2 reacts differently with hot and cold NaOH (aq) giving different products in different oxidation states.
- Sulfuric acid reacts with NaCl, NaBr and NaI, but only NaBr and NaI are a strong enough reducing agents to reduce the H_2SO_4.

3.4 *d*-block chemistry

- Transition elements lose their *s*-electrons first when they react and have partially filled *d*-orbitals in their ions.
- The elements each have a range of oxidation states.
- They form complexes by bonding with ligands.
- Complexes absorb some frequencies of light, and the reflected light makes them coloured.
- They can be used as catalysts in many reactions

3.5 Chemical kinetics

- Rates can be measured by studying how any factor (pressure, volume or colour) changes over time.
- The order of reaction gives the effect of each concentration on rate.
- The reaction rate can be calculated from the rate equation, which combines concentrations, orders and rate constant.
- The substances and orders in the rate equation give the rate determining step (slowest step) of a reaction mechanism.
- The Arrhenius equation can be used to quantify the effect of temperature on the rate constant.

3.6 Enthalpy changes for solids and solutions

- There are many standard enthalpy changes and they all start with or form 1 mole of substance.
- Energy changes can be combined in energy cycles to work out overall energy changes.
- Stable compounds have negative enthalpies of formation.

3.7 Entropy and feasibility of reactions

- Entropy is a measure of the degrees of freedom in a system, so gases have higher entropy than liquids and solids.
- Gibbs free energy combines enthalpy and entropy, $\Delta G = \Delta H - T\Delta S$.
- For a reaction to be feasible, ΔG must be negative.

3.8 Equilibrium constants

- All equilibrium constants have the products divided by the reactants.
- K_p is in terms of pressure, and K_c is in terms of concentration.
- Equilibrium constants often have units which derive from the units of concentration or pressure.
- Equilibrium constants are constant, except when the temperature changes.

3.9 Acid-base equilibria

- Acids are proton donors, and bases are proton acceptors, with weak acids dissociating partially and strong acids dissociating fully.
- $pH = -\log [H^+]$, and for a strong acid $[H^+] = [acid]$.
- K_a shows the strength of acids – a larger K_a means a stronger acid, and it can be used to calculate the pH of a weak acid.
- $K_w = [H^+] \times [OH^-]$ and this allows us to calculate the pH of a strong base.
- During acid-base titrations the pH changes unevenly, with different patterns depending on the strength of the acid and base.
- Indicators are weak acids or bases that change colour. An indicator is chosen that changes colour completely in the vertical region of a titration curve
- Buffers are solutions of weak acids and their salts, which keep pH constant.
- The salt of a weak acid will be basic, and the salt of a weak base will be acidic.

U4 Knowledge and Understanding

Analysing and Building Molecules

Unit 4 builds on the foundation ideas of spectroscopy and basic organic chemistry introduced at AS level and goes on to explore these concepts in more detail. Modern organic chemistry relies for its understanding on the mechanistic background to reactions which, in turn, closely link to polarity in bonds – particularly bonds between atoms of carbon, hydrogen, oxygen, nitrogen and halogens. Finding the structure of organic compounds now depends much more on infrared, NMR spectroscopy and mass spectrometry, rather than the more traditional elemental analysis and functional group reactions. The latter though, do still have an important role and this is explored in the various topics in this unit.

Revised it!

Basic notes | Good grasp | Fully revised

4.1 Stereoisomerism

It is very important to realise that few molecules are 'flat' and the position that the bonds take up in space is vitally important.

→ **p48–49** →

4.2 Aromaticity

At A2 level we meet the idea that molecules need not be straight-chained, branch-chained or are ring molecules that have aliphatic reactions (alicyclic compounds). Aromatic compounds have much greater ring stability than alicyclic compounds, leading to different reactions.

→ **p50–53** →

4.3 Alcohols and phenols

We have met alcohols in the AS year, and this study is now extended to include phenols, where the OH group is bonded directly to the benzene ring. The reactions of these two groups of compounds are compared.

→ **p54–56** →

4.4 Aldehydes and ketones

These are very important compounds that contain the carbonyl (C=O) group. One way of making these carbonyl compounds is by the oxidation of alcohols.

→ **p57–59** →

Basic notes   Good grasp   Fully revised

4.5 Carboxylic acids and their derivatives

Carboxylic acids contain the COOH group. Substitution of the OH group can produce amides, acid (acyl) halides and esters.

→ **p60–64** →

4.6 Amines

An amine contains an NH_2 group directly bonded to a carbon atom. They form the building blocks for many other larger and biologically important molecules.

→ **p65–68** →

4.7 Amino acids, peptides and proteins

Amino acids contain both NH_2 and COOH groups and can be condensed together to provide the starting materials for polypeptides and proteins.

→ **p69–70** →

4.8 Organic synthesis and analysis

It is very important to be able to link reactions together to give sequences, which show how particular compounds can be synthesised. The structure of an organic compound can be found by chemical analysis and by instrumental techniques such as NMR, mass spectroscopy and infrared absorption spectroscopy.

→ **p71–79** →

4.1 Stereoisomerism

Stereoisomerism is about how atoms and groups are arranged in space. As the name suggests, stereoisomers must be isomers that differ in some way because of their spatial arrangement. They must have the same structural formula (arrangement of atoms) but differ in the way the bonds are arranged in space. There are two forms of stereoisomerism – E/Z isomerism and optical isomerism.

E-Z isomerism

You will have met $E-Z$ isomerism before at AS level but it also occurs in this Unit. Compounds showing this type of isomerism have at least one carbon-to-carbon double bond with different atoms or groups bonded to these carbon atoms. These atoms or groups can be the same or different but there cannot be two identical atoms or groups the same bonded to the same carbon atom. The simplest illustration is one where each 'end' of the double bond has the same atoms or groups.

(E)– 1,2–dichloroethene   (Z)– 1,2–dichloroethene

If the two atoms or groups are 'opposite' each other, then it is the E- isomer and if they are not opposite each other then it is called the Z- isomer.

Of course, it is not necessary to have the atoms or groups the same. Let us look at the stereoisomers of 1-chloro-2-bromopropene, $CH_3CBr=CHCl$. These can be drawn as the E- or the Z- forms.

(E)–1–bromo–2–chloropropene   (Z)–1–bromo–2–chloropropene

These are obviously stereoisomers, as the atoms/groups have different spatial arrangements. There are rules for deciding which of the two is the E-isomer and which one is the Z-isomer and these are discussed in the AS Study and Revision guide.

Until recently this type of isomerism was called **geometrical isomerism** and the E-isomerism was 'trans' and the Z-isomer the 'cis' form.

Sometimes examination questions ask 'why does this type of stereoisomerism occur?' One end of the double bond cannot rotate relative to its other end – strictly, an acceptable form of words is 'there is no rotation about a double bond'.

Grade boost

Be very careful when describing stereoisomerism. It is incorrect to say that 'stereoisomers have the same molecular or empirical formulae but differ in the spatial arrangement of their atoms'. Compounds with the same molecular or empirical formulae are not necessarily in the same family of compounds.

Grade boost

If you are asked to explain why $E-Z$ isomerism occurs beware of writing 'because the double bond cannot rotate'. Of course it can completely rotate, but the important point is that one end cannot rotate relative to the other end.

quickfire

㉚ Draw the structural formula of hex-1-ene and state why this compound cannot show $E-Z$ isomerism.

quickfire

㉛ Draw the structural formula of (Z)-pent-2-ene.

Stereoisomerism is about the arrangement of groups or atoms in a compound in space. In E-Z stereoisomerism we have looked at the different arrangements about a carbon-to-carbon double bond. In this section, we look at the position when a carbon atom is bonded to four different groups or atoms by single bonds.

Optical isomerism

The 'central' carbon atom that has four different groups or atoms bonded to it is called a **chiral centre** (or chiral carbon atom). In older books we would see this described as an asymmetric carbon atom. There are two different spatial arrangements of this chiral centre and its four bonded atoms. These two arrangements are mirror images of each other.

As well as being mirror images of each other they affect the plane of plane polarised light and, because of this, they are called **optical isomers** or **enantiomers**. One of these enantiomers will rotate the plane of plane polarised light to the left and the other one rotates it to the right. It is not necessary to know why this occurs or the change in direction produced by a particular isomer. If equal molar quantities of each enantiomer are in a mixture in solution, then the rotation one way is balanced out by the rotation the other way. The result is a solution that appears to be optically inactive, i.e. it has no effect on the plane of plane polarised light– we call this a **racemic mixture**. Chiral compounds are very important in biochemistry where enzymes can only work if the shape of the molecule is correct.

Questions on this topic often ask candidates to identity a chiral centre in the given formula of a compound. Very often this chiral centre is then identified by an asterisk.

Common compounds with a chiral centre

2-hydroxypropanoic acid   2-aminopropanoic acid

These two compounds are very useful for examiners because they can form part of longer questions.

2-Aminopropanoic acid is an α-amino acid and a question can then lead on to zwitterions and dipeptide formation.

Key Terms

Chiral centre = central carbon atom that has four different groups or atoms bonded to it.

Enantiomer = a molecule that is a mirror image of another molecule and rotates the plane of plane polarised light.

Racemic mixture = a solution that appears to be optically inactive that contains equimolar quantities of each enantiomer.

Grade boost

Beware of questions that ask you to identify chiral centres. Some molecules have more than chiral centre!

Grade boost

When looking for chiral centres, the important point to remember is that the chiral carbon atom must have *four different* groups or atoms bonded directly to it. As a result, any carbon atom that has a double bond to another atom cannot be a chiral centre.

quickfire

③② Identify any chiral centres in the formula of the compound below.

$$H_3C - \underset{\underset{SH}{|}}{\overset{\overset{H}{|}}{C}} - \underset{\underset{Br}{|}}{\overset{\overset{H}{|}}{C}} - COOH$$

4.2 Aromaticity

The structure of benzene

The molecular formula of benzene is C_6H_6 and X-ray studies show that the carbon atoms form a flat hexagon with the C–C–C bond angle 120^0. The Kekulé structure of benzene shows an alternating system of single and double carbon-to-carbon bonds around the ring. However, if this was true benzene would decolourise bromine water, like an alkene, and this does not happen. It would also be a reactive compound, which it is not.

Kekulé form   delocalised form

Evidence suggests that benzene contains a **delocalised** electron structure with a π- cloud of electrons around the ring. Support for this is that each carbon-to-carbon bond has the same length and that this is intermediate in size between the lengths of the double and single bonds.

Pointer

Although benzene does not react with aqueous bromine (bromine water) more reactive aromatic compounds will react with it. However, these result in substitution products not addition products.

The delocalisation energy of benzene

The reaction of cyclohexene (a six membered ring with one carbon-to-carbon double bond) with hydrogen to produce cyclohexane, gives out 120 kJ mol^{-1} (ΔH = -120 kJ mol^{-1}).

A similar hydrogenation of cyclohexa-1,3-diene to produce cyclohexane produces -240 kJ mol^{-1}. If benzene contained three double bonds (the Kekulé structure) then we would expect a value of about -360 kJ mol^{-1}, when cyclohexane is made by hydrogenation. In fact, the value turns out to be -208 kJ mol^{-1}. This figure suggests that benzene does *not* have the Kekulé structure and is more stable than the alternating double bond–single bond structure. The difference between the 'expected' and found values (152 kJ mol^{-1}) is called the delocalisation (or resonance) energy.

These energy values provide further evidence for the delocalised structure of benzene.

Grade boost

Three pieces of evidence for the delocalised structure of benzene are:
- All bond lengths are the same.
- The enthalpy of hydrogenation means that benzene is more stable than suggested by the Kekulé structure.
- Benzene tends to react by substitution rather than by addition.

The resistance of benzene to addition reactions

Alkenes react mainly by addition, for example the reaction of ethene with hydrogen chloride to give chloroethane.

$$CH_2=CH_2 + HCl \longrightarrow CH_3CH_2Cl$$

However, benzene finds it difficult to react by addition. This is more evidence in favour of the stable delocalised electron ring structure. If addition occurred then the stable π- electron cloud would be lost. The preferred way for benzene to react is by the substitution of the hydrogen atoms, as this would retain the delocalised structure of the molecule.

The nitration, halogenation and alkylation of benzene

Benzene usually reacts by substitution so that the stability of the π-electron system is maintained. Since the π-cloud of electrons is negatively charged, the most common reaction of benzene involves **electrophilic substitution**. The 'incoming' group needs to be an electrophile and this is usually made from the reactants 'in situ' – this means that it is made and reacts as it is formed.

The nitration of benzene

Nitrobenzene, $C_6H_5NO_2$, is made by reacting benzene with a mixture of concentrated nitric and sulfuric acids at 50°C or below. If the temperature rises above this temperature then some dinitration can occur – giving 1,3-dinitrobenzene, which is a pale yellow solid.

The first stage of the mechanism is the production of the nitronium ion, NO_2^+, (sometimes called the nitryl cation), which acts as the electrophile. In the next stage the nitronium ion reacts with benzene giving nitrobenzene.

$$HNO_3 + 2H_2SO_4 \rightleftharpoons NO_2^+ + H_3O^+ + 2HSO_4^-$$

quickfire

33 If 0.1 mole of benzene is completely nitrated to give only nitrobenzene, what is the mass of nitrobenzene produced?
[A_r: H = 1; C = 12; N = 14; O = 16]

》 Pointer
Strong sunlight is not advisable for this reaction as the ultraviolet light may encourage an addition reaction between benzene and the halogen.

The halogenation of benzene

Bromobenzene, C_6H_5Br, is made from benzene and bromine in the presence of a catalyst at room temperature. The catalyst often used is iron(III) bromide, although books may list other suitable materials. Sometimes the catalyst is described as a 'halogen carrier' and this would be acceptable in an examination answer. You will often find books describing the reaction as being done in the dark – but, of course, if this was taken literally you would not be able to see what was going on! The correct description is probably 'out of direct sunlight'.

Key Term

Polarisation = an unequal electron distribution in a covalent bond.

3a A scientist reacted 0.20 mole of benzene with bromine. He obtained 24.0 g of bromobenzene (M_r 157). Calculate the percentage yield of bromobenzene.

b In another experiment the scientist reported that the yield of bromobenzene was 37.5 g and this represented a percentage yield of 68%. Calculate the starting mass of benzene used.

Grade boost

When writing mechanisms always check that the curly arrow is coming from the benzene ring and not from the nitro-group or bromine atom. It is a common error to write it the other way round.

As with the nitration of benzene, this halogenation is an electrophilic substitution reaction. The catalyst causes **polarisation** of the Br – Br bond followed by reaction with the benzene ring.

The two ions formed H^+ and $FeBr_4^-$ can then react together to give hydrogen bromide gas and iron(III) bromide. Hydrogen bromide gas is lost from the reaction mixture – hence the need for the reaction to be carried out in a fume cupboard. The iron(III) bromide can then carry out the reaction again – hence its 'catalytic' action.

If chlorobenzene is required then chlorine needs to be bubbled through benzene 'in the dark' with iron(III) chloride, $FeCl_3$, or aluminium chloride, $AlCl_3$, used as a catalyst.

The alkylation of benzene

This reaction is often called the Friedel–Crafts reaction, after the scientists who discovered it. The term 'alkylation' means the substitution of an alkyl group such as methyl, $-CH_3$, or ethyl, $-CH_2CH_3$. This reaction is carried out in a similar way to the halogenation of benzene but, for example, chloromethane is used in place of bromine. Again, a catalyst is used – the commonest one is aluminium chloride.

The mechanism is again electrophilic substitution and is similar to those given above.

The alkaline hydrolysis of chloroalkanes and chlorobenzene

A chloroalkane, such as 1-chlorobutane, reacts easily with sodium hydroxide solution when the mixture is refluxed, giving butan-1-ol as the organic product.

$$CH_3CH_2CH_2CH_2Cl + NaOH \longrightarrow CH_3CH_2CH_2CH_2OH + NaCl$$

In Unit 2 you are required to know that the mechanism of this reaction is nucleophilic substitution.

However benzene, with its stable π-ring system of electrons is not very likely to react with a nucleophile. The previous pages have reminded you that benzene tends to react mainly with electrophiles. In chlorobenzene, the bond between the chlorine atom and the carbon atom is stronger than the aliphatic C-Cl bond found in 1-chlorobutane.

Bond	Bond energy / kJ mol^{-1}
Aliphatic C-Cl	346
Aromatic C-Cl	399

This stronger bond between carbon and chlorine in chlorobenzene results from the non-bonding lone pairs overlapping with ring π-system of electrons. The resulting bond needs much more energy to be broken. It is possible to make phenol from chlorobenzene but forcing conditions of temperature and pressure are required, not just simple refluxing at around 100°C.

As a result phenol cannot be made from chlorobenzene except under extreme conditions, which are not economically viable. In industry phenol is generally made from (1-methylethyl)benzene (cumene). This has the advantage that propanone is a co-product of the reaction.

Grade boost

A weak area for many candidates in the examination is the description of practical work. Candidates may be asked to describe what is meant by 'refluxing'. Your response should state that evaporation and condensation are occurring and that the condensed material returns to the flask where the reaction is going on. If you do not say 'returns' to the flask, then you could be describing distillation!

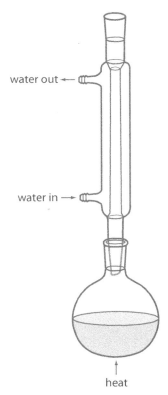

Grade boost

Candidates lose marks by not stating that aqueous sodium hydroxide is used to react with the halogenoalkane. The use of an alcoholic solution of the alkali gives mainly the corresponding alkene as the product.

quickfire

㉞ Give the displayed formula of the product obtained by heating this compound

$$\text{benzene-}CH_2-\underset{\underset{H}{|}}{\overset{\overset{CH_3}{|}}{C}}-CH_2Br$$

with aqueous sodium hydroxide.

4a State the name of the organic product made when 1-bromopropane reacts with aqueous sodium hydroxide.

b Give the displayed formula of the compound produced when phenylethanone, $C_6H_5COCH_3$, is reduced by sodium tetrahydridoborate(III).

c Explain why the compound produced in (b) can exist as enantiomers.

4.3 Alcohols and phenols

Methods of forming primary and secondary alcohols

Forming alcohols from halogenoalkanes

A halogenoalkane is heated under reflux with an aqueous solution of an alkali (often sodium hydroxide). For example, pentan-1-ol can be obtained from 1-chloropentane. The equation for the reaction can be written as a full chemical equation or as an ionic equation.

$$CH_3CH_2CH_2CH_2CH_2Cl + NaOH \longrightarrow CH_3CH_2CH_2CH_2CH_2OH + NaCl$$
$$CH_3CH_2CH_2CH_2CH_2Cl + OH^- \longrightarrow CH_3CH_2CH_2CH_2CH_2OH + Cl^-$$

The mechanism for this reaction is described as nucleophilic substitution and is mentioned in Unit 2 but it could be requested in a question on the Unit 4 paper. Chlorobenzene cannot easily react in this way – the reasons for this are described in the previous section.

Forming alcohols from aldehydes and ketones

The reduction of aldehydes and ketones gives primary alcohols and secondary alcohols respectively. This is the reverse of the reactions studied in Unit 2 where primary and secondary alcohols are oxidized to aldehydes and ketones respectively by using acidified potassium dichromate solution. These reactions forming alcohols are reduction processes and the usual reducing agent is sodium tetrahydridoborate(III), $NaBH_4$, dissolved in water. This compound is sometimes called 'sodium borohydride'. The equations for these reactions are quite complicated and it is acceptable to represent the reducing agent $NaBH_4$ as [H] and to balance the equation in the usual way.

$$CH_3CH_2CH_2CHO + 2[H] \longrightarrow CH_3CH_2CH_2CH_2OH$$
butanal $\qquad\qquad\qquad$ butan-1-ol

$$CH_3CH_2CH_2COCH_3 + 2[H] \longrightarrow CH_3CH_2CH_2CH(OH)CH_3$$
pentan-2-one $\qquad\qquad\qquad$ pentan-2-ol

Reactions of primary and secondary alcohols

Reaction with hydrogen halides

The reaction of primary and secondary alcohols with hydrogen halides produces halogenoalkanes. These reactions do not always give good yields and are often slow and reversible. The method used depends on the halogen present in the product.

Chlorination One method is to pass hydrogen chloride gas into the alcohol using anhydrous zinc chloride as a catalyst.

$$CH_3(CH_2)_4CH_2OH \xrightarrow[ZnCl_2]{HCl} CH_3(CH_2)_4CH_2Cl$$

Chlorination can also be carried out using phosphorus(V) chloride, PCl_5, or sulfur dichloride oxide, $SOCl_2$, as the source of chlorine.

Bromination The usual method is to heat a mixture of the alcohol, potassium bromide and 50% sulfuric acid.

$$CH_3CH_2CH_2CH_2OH + KBr + H_2SO_4 \longrightarrow CH_3CH_2CH_2CH_2Br + K\,HSO_4 + H_2O$$

Iodination One method is to warm the alcohol with a mixture of red phosphorus and iodine.

Reaction with ethanoyl chloride

Esters are rapidly formed by reacting together a primary or secondary alcohol and ethanoyl chloride, CH_3COCl. Hydrogen chloride is given off as a gaseous co-product. This enables a higher yield to be produced than when using a carboxylic acid but is not cost-effective as an industrial method.

phenylmethyl ethanoate

Reaction with carboxylic acids

This is a very common method of producing an ester. The alcohol and the carboxylic acid are refluxed together with a little concentrated sulfuric acid, which acts as a catalyst. Any acid that remains is neutralised by using sodium hydrogencarbonate solution and the ester-containing layer is then removed by use of a separating funnel. After drying, the ester layer is distilled and the ester collected at its boiling temperature.

Key Term

Ester = compound that contains the group:

Grade boost

The chlorination of an alcohol by using $SOCl_2$ is a good method because the other products, SO_2 and HCl are both gases and are lost from the reaction mixture. This does mean, however, that a fume cupboard needs to be used for this reaction.

quickfire

(35) State the name of the carboxylic acid that reacts with methanol to produce an ester that has the formula shown below.

quickfire

(36) Write the displayed formula of any ester that has the molecular formula $C_4H_8O_2$.

The acidity of phenol and its reactions with bromine, ethanoyl chloride and iron(III) chloride

The acidity of phenol

Phenols are benzene ring compounds where the hydroxyl group is bonded directly to the ring.

phenol   4-methylphenol   pentachlorophenol

The presence of the benzene ring tends to weaken the O-H bond. This means that phenols are weakly acidic in aqueous solution as protons are lost.

The phenoxide ion is more stable than expected as the negative charge tends to be spread 'around' the ring. When compared with carboxylic acids, phenols are generally much weaker acids but are stronger acids than alcohols. When carboxylic acids react with sodium carbonate or sodium hydrogencarbonate, carbon dioxide is produced as a colourless gas, showing as gas bubbles in the mixture. Phenol is not acidic enough to react in this way and no bubbles are seen.

The reaction of phenol with bromine

Phenol is more reactive than benzene and will react with bromine (generally carried out in aqueous solution) to produce 2,4,6-tribromophenol as an immediate white precipitate. The bromine is decolourised. This reaction can be used as a test for phenol.

The reaction of phenol with ethanoyl chloride

Phenol will react with ethanoyl chloride to produce the ester phenyl ethanoate, and hydrogen chloride. This is a slower reaction than the corresponding reaction of an alcohol and ethanoyl chloride.

The reaction of phenol with iron(III) chloride

Another test for phenols is to add aqueous iron(III) chloride solution, when a purple coloration is seen in the solution.

quickfire

③⑦ Give the equation for the dissociation of 2,4-dimethylphenol into hydrogen ions (protons) and the anion of 2,4-dimethylphenol.

Grade boost

When testing for phenol using aqueous bromine, the usual method is to add aqueous bromine dropwise to the phenol solution. The bromine is at first decolourised and then, when more aqueous bromine is added, a white precipitate of 2,4,6-tribromophenol is seen. If phenol was added to aqueous bromine, it would be difficult to see the immediate decolourisation of the bromine.

quickfire

③⑧ Give the empirical formula of the ester phenyl ethanoate.

4.4 Aldehydes and ketones

The oxidation of primary and secondary alcohols

Some alcohol chemistry has been studied during the AS year of the course and this included their oxidation. Details are provided in the AS Study and Revision Guide. The usual oxidising agent is acidified potassium (or sodium) dichromate (acidified dichromate) sometimes shown as $H^+/Cr_2O_7^{2-}$. During the reaction, the orange colour of the acidified dichromate is replaced by the green colour of Cr^{3+}(aq) ions. In writing equations, the use of [O] to represent the oxidising agent is acceptable.

Primary alcohols are oxidised to an aldehyde and then, by further oxidation, to a carboxylic acid. For example, propan-1-ol is oxidised to propanal and then to propanoic acid.

$$CH_3CH_2CH_2OH + [O] \longrightarrow CH_3CH_2CHO + H_2O$$
$$CH_3CH_2CHO + [O] \longrightarrow CH_3CH_2COOH$$

Secondary alcohols are oxidised in the same way to a **ketone**. For example, propan-2-ol is oxidised to propanone.

$$CH_3CH(OH)CH_3 + [O] \longrightarrow CH_3COCH_3 + H_2O$$

Distinguishing between aldehydes and ketones

Aldehydes can act as reducing agents as they can be further oxidised to carboxylic acids but ketones are not susceptible to further oxidation. Some reagents that are reduced by an aldehyde can be used to distinguish between these carbonyl compounds.

Tollens' reagent

A little of the suspected aldehyde or ketone is added to the reagent and the tube containing the mixture is placed in warm water. If an aldehyde is present a silver mirror is seen on the inside of the tube. A ketone does not react in this way.

$$Ag^+(aq) + e^- \longrightarrow Ag(s)$$

Fehling's reagent

When warmed in the presence of a suspected aldehyde the Cu^{2+} ions are reduced to a red-brown precipitate of copper(I) oxide, Cu_2O. Ketones do not react with either reagent. A simple equation for this reduction could be

$$2Cu^{2+} + 2OH^- + 2e^- \longrightarrow Cu_2O(s) + H_2O(l)$$

5 Here are the names of five compounds:

- ethanedioic acid
- cyclohexene
- propane-1,2-diol
- pentan-2-one
- hexanal.

Select which of these compounds will:

a decolourise aqueous bromine

b react with Fehling's solution

c react with acidified dichromate but **not** with Tollens' reagent

d *not* react with acidified dichromate or give bubbles of CO_2 with sodium hydrogencarbonate

e *not* react with acidified dichromate but does give bubbles of CO_2 with sodium hydrogencarbonate.

>> *Pointer*

This is a very important
section for examiners, as
they can ask about the
mechanism and then ask
further questions about the
hydroxynitrile and compounds
formed from it.

Grade boost

If the question starts with
ethanal, you will end up with
2-hydroxypropanoic acid after
hydrolysis of the product.
The examiner could then ask
about this acid as it contains
a chiral centre and is both an
acid and an alcohol!

quicKpire

(39) The formula of the product
formed by the nucleophilic
addition of hydrogen
cyanide to an aldehyde or
ketone is $CH_3CH_2C(OH)$
$(CH_3CH_2)CN$. Give the
name of the starting
aldehyde or ketone.

The reduction of aldehydes and ketones

Aldehydes and ketones can be reduced to primary and secondary alcohols
respectively. The usual reducing agent is sodium tetrahydridoborate(III),
$NaBH_4$, in aqueous solution. This reaction has been described in section 4.3
Alcohols and phenols.

The addition of hydrogen cyanide to carbonyl compounds

There are several classes of compounds that contain carbonyl (C=O) groups.
In this course the term carbonyl compound refers to aldehydes and ketones.
The reaction of hydrogen cyanide with an aldehyde or a ketone is a very
important step in organic synthesis. The reaction forms a way of 'ascending
the **homologous series**'. This means creating a new carbon-to-carbon bond
so that the carbon chain length is increased. A typical reaction is the reaction of
hydrogen cyanide with ethanal.

The product is 2-hydroxypropanenitrile and as such, is not a particularly
useful material. However, hydrolysis of the nitrile group, often carried out by
warming with dilute sulfuric acid is 2-hydroxypropanoic acid (or lactic acid).
This can be converted to other compounds.

The mechanism of the reaction

Aldehydes and ketones contain a polar carbonyl group, $C^{\delta+}= O^{\delta-}$. This allows
them to be attacked by nucleophiles or electrophiles. Hydrogen cyanide
is a weak acid and there are relatively few cyanide ions available to attack
the carbonyl compound. A little sodium cyanide is added to the mixture to
provide more cyanide ions. The first stage in the mechanism is the attack
of a cyanide ion (the nucleophile) on the $\delta+$ carbon atom of the carbonyl
group. Increased polarisation of the carbonyl group then allows a hydrogen
ion from the hydrogen cyanide to bond with the resulting negatively charged
oxygen atom to give an alcohol group. This mechanism is called nucleophilic
addition because the CN^- nucleophile initially attacks the $\delta+$ carbon atom and
the hydrogen ion is then attached to the oxygen 'atom'. Addition of HCN has
effectively occurred across the carbon to oxygen double bond.

Identifying aldehydes and ketones

The tests with both Tollens' and Fehling's reagents are positive for an aldehyde and **not** a ketone because of the presence of an 'oxidisable' hydrogen atom in an aldehyde. An aldehyde can be distinguished from a ketone by warming it with the acidified dichromate reagent. Since an aldehyde can be oxidised to a carboxylic acid, it will reduce the orange acidified dichromate to a green solution that contains aqueous Cr^{3+} ions. Another reagent that can be used to identify an aldehyde is acidified potassium manganate(VII) solution (H^+/MnO_4^-). This purple solution is reduced by an aldehyde to a colourless solution that contain aqueous Mn(II) ions. A ketone will not react with either acidified dichromate or acidified manganate(VII) solutions.

Any test that is positive for **just** the carbonyl group will be given by both aldehydes and ketones. The only test that you are required to know is the test that uses a solution of 2,4-dinitrophenylhydrazine (shortened to 2,4 DNP or Brady's reagent). It is not necessary to know the formula of 2,4-DNP or the formula of the product obtained when an aldehyde or ketone reacts with it. However, you do need to know that the reaction is nucleophilic addition followed by the elimination of a small molecule (water). This is often shortened to nucleophilic addition–elimination and sometimes also simply described as a condensation reaction.

The aldehyde or ketone will react with 2,4-dinitrophenylhydrazine to give a distinctive orange-red precipitate. This is filtered off and purified. The melting temperature of the solid is then taken and compared with textbook values of melting temperatures. The value will then identify the starting aldehyde or ketone. Many aldehydes and ketones are liquids of fairly low boiling point and their flammable nature often makes it difficult to identify them simply, safely and accurately just from their boiling temperature. The melting temperature range of the 2,4-DNP derivative is suitable for most melting temperature determinations, perhaps 75°C to about 175°C. An example of this is ethanal.

Ethanal boils at 21°C but its 2,4-DNP derivative melts at 147°C

Tests for the $CH_3C=O$ group in ketones

Compounds that contain $CH_3C=O$ include propanone and butanone. When these are reacted with an alkaline solution of iodine (or an aqueous mixture of sodium chlorate(I) and potassium iodide) a yellow precipitate of triiodomethane (iodoform), CHI_3, is formed. This test (the triiodomethane reaction) is also given by compounds that contain the $CH_3CH(OH)$ group, as this is oxidised to the $CH_3C=O$ group during the reaction. This means that ethanol and propan-2-ol also react in this way but not propan-1-ol.

Grade boost

The test for the $CH_3C=O$ group in ketones is sometimes called the 'iodoform' reaction, after the traditional name for triiodomethane. Ensure that you do not use triiodomethane (iodoform) as one of the reactants. It is the product in the test!

quickfire

(40) Identify which of these compounds will undergo the triiodomethane reaction.
(a) pentan-2-ol
(b) hexan-3-ol
(c) 1,3-dichloropropanone
(d) methanal
(e) 2-methylphenol

4.5 Carboxylic acids and their derivatives

The relative acidity of carboxylic acids, phenols, alcohols and water

A compound can act as an **acid** if it produces hydrogen ions, $H^+(aq)$ when it 'dissolves' in water, for example

$$CH_3COOH(aq) + H_2O(l) \longrightarrow CH_3COO^-(aq) + H_3O^+(aq)$$

The equation shows the hydrogen ion as its hydrated form, $H_3O^+(aq)$ but we often use $H^+(aq)$, for simplicity. The extent to which hydrogen ions are formed gives a measure of acidity. In Unit 3 you studied K_a, which is a measure of the extent to which this dissociation into ions has occurred. In simple terms, we can look at the pH of aqueous solutions (of the same concentration) to compare acid strengths of various types of compounds. An example of this is shown in the table.

Pointer

The equation for the neutralisation of phenol by sodium hydroxide is
$C_6H_5OH + NaOH$
$\longrightarrow C_6H_5O^-Na^+ + H_2O$

compound	pH
ethanoic acid	2.9
phenol	5.5
water	7.0
ethanol	~ 8.5

You will see that ethanoic acid is the strongest acid and that water and ethanol are not really acidic at all. So what are the reasons for these variations in acidity?

ETHANOIC ACID When added to water, hydrogen ions and ethanoate ions are formed.

$$CH_3COOH_{(aq)} \rightleftharpoons CH_3COO^-_{(aq)} + H^+_{(aq)}$$

The extent to which are hydrogen ions are formed depends partly on the stability of the starting materials and products. The ethanoate ion (and similar ions formed from other carboxylic acids), are more stable than the ions formed from ethanol and water, because the negative charge can be delocalised across several atoms.

Grade boost

Make sure that, if the question asks for observations, you give observations not results. For example 'fizzing' is an observation but 'carbon dioxide is produced' is not.

$$\left[H_3C - C \underset{\diagdown O}{\overset{\diagup O}{<}} \right]^-$$

PHENOL The phenoxide ion, $C_6H_5O^-$, is more stable than the ions formed by water and ethanol because of the delocalisation of the negative charge around the π-electron ring system of the benzene.

ETHANOL There is little tendency for ethanol molecules to ionise as the ethoxide ion, $C_2H_5O^-$, is not stabilised by delocalisation.

Both phenol and ethanoic acid can be neutralised by an alkali such as sodium hydroxide, giving a salt. However, only a carboxylic acid is sufficiently acidic to produce carbon dioxide when a carbonate is added. This test provides a way of showing the difference in the relative acidities of these compounds.

Forming carboxylic acids by oxidation

The oxidation of primary alcohols and aldehydes

Primary alcohols (but not secondary alcohols) can be oxidised to carboxylic acids using a suitable oxidising agent. In the following equation, the oxidising agent is represented by [O].

$$R-\underset{\underset{H}{|}}{\overset{\overset{H}{|}}{C}}-OH \xrightarrow{[O]} R-C\overset{\displaystyle O}{\underset{\displaystyle H}{<}} \xrightarrow{[O]} R-C\overset{\displaystyle O}{\underset{\displaystyle OH}{<}}$$

The usual oxidising agent is acidified potassium dichromate solution – a solution of potassium dichromate in strong aqueous sulfuric acid. This is sometimes represented by the 'formula' $H^+(aq)/Cr_2O_7^{2-}(aq)$. To produce the carboxylic acid, the alcohol or aldehyde is refluxed with an **excess** of the oxidising agent. The colour change is from orange to green as dichromate ions, $Cr_2O_7^{2-}$, are reduced to green chromium(III), $Cr^{3+}(aq)$ ions , but of course an excess of the orange dichromate is present.

Alternatively, a strong oxidising agent such as acidified potassium manganate(VII) solution can be used. This solution of potassium manganate(VII) in strong aqueous sulfuric acid can be represented by the 'formula' $H^+(aq)/MnO_4^-(aq)$. This mixture is refluxed with the alcohol or aldehyde. The purple manganate(VII) ions are reduced to 'colourless' $Mn^{2+}(aq)$ ions. This colour change may be difficult to notice as an excess of the manganate(VII) is used. In either preparation the carboxylic acid is distilled from the reaction mixture and purified.

The oxidation of alkylbenzenes

Aromatic carboxylic acids, such as benzenecarboxylic acid (benzoic acid), C_6H_5COOH, can be obtained by refluxing together an alkylbenzene with alkaline potassium manganate(VII) solution. An alkylbenzene is a benzene hydrocarbon with e.g. a methyl group substituted in place of a hydrogen atom. An overall equation is

$$\underset{\text{CH}_3}{\bigcirc} \xrightarrow{3\,[O]} \underset{\text{COOH}}{\bigcirc} + H_2O$$

The purple solution of potassium manganate(VII) is reduced to brown manganese(IV) oxide, seen as a brown sludge. Since this reaction takes place in an alkaline solution the organic product is, for example, sodium benzenecarboxylate (sodium benzoate), $C_6H_5COO^-Na^+$. The mixture is then acidified with a dilute acid (e.g. HCl(aq)) when white crystals of benzenecarboxylic acid are produced.

Grade boost

Candidates often have trouble in clearly giving the name of the reducing agent whose formula is LiAlH$_4$. Although examiners have tended to be lenient with such a tricky name – do try and learn that it is lithium tetrahydridoaluminate(III).

The reduction of carboxylic acids

Carboxylic acids are stable compounds and a powerful reducing agent is needed to reverse the oxidation process that gave them and to produce aldehydes and primary alcohols. The reducing agent that is used is lithium tetrahydridoaluminate(III), LiAlH$_4$. This compound reacts violently with water and so it is dissolved in a non-aqueous solvent (usually ethoxyethane). A chemical equation is required for this reaction but the reducing agent can be represented by [H].

$$CH_3-C\overset{O}{\underset{OH}{\diagdown}} \xrightarrow{4\,[H]} CH_3-C\overset{OH}{\underset{H}{|}}H + H_2O$$

Decarboxylation = the loss of a carboxyl group (literally CO$_2$). A decarboxylation reaction leads to a reduction in the length of the carbon chain.

≫ Pointer

In general, decarboxylation reactions give poor yields. Although we can write a simple equation for the reaction (and this is all that is needed for the examination), many other reactions are also occurring. Bond fission occurs at several places in the carbon chain, giving a variety of products.

quickfire

㊷ State the name of the alkane obtained if sodium hexanoate is strongly heated with sodalime.

The decarboxylation of carboxylic acids

When a carboxylic acid (or more usually its sodium salt) is strongly heated with an alkali such as solid sodium hydroxide or sodalime, **decarboxylation** occurs and an alkane is produced, together with a carbonate. An example is the decarboxylation of sodium propanoate. Sodalime is a mixture prepared by heating together sodium hydroxide and calcium oxide. However, for simplicity, in equations we represent its formula as NaOH.

$$CH_3CH_2COO^-Na^+(s) + NaOH(s) \longrightarrow C_2H_6(g) + Na_2CO_3(s)$$
$$\text{ethane}$$

If the salt of an aromatic acid is used, then an aromatic hydrocarbon is the organic product

$$C_6H_5COO^-Na^+(s) + NaOH(s) \longrightarrow C_6H_6(g) + Na_2CO_3(s)$$
$$\text{sodium benzenecarboxylate} \qquad \text{benzene}$$

This reaction is an example of 'descending the homologous series' – this phrase means a reaction that reduces the length of the carbon chain.

If the calcium salt of the carboxylic acid is strongly heated, then decarboxylation also occurs and the product is an aldehyde or ketone. For example the decarboxylation of calcium ethanoate gives propanone.

$$(CH_3COO)_2Ca \longrightarrow CH_3COCH_3 + CaCO_3$$

The conversion of carboxylic acids to esters and their hydrolysis

An ester can be prepared by reacting together a primary or secondary alcohol and a carboxylic acid. A little concentrated sulfuric acid is generally used as a catalyst. The mixture is refluxed – often using a water bath or an electrical heater because of the dangers of fire from direct heating. Any remaining acid is then neutralised using sodium hydrogencarbonate solution. The two layers are separated by use of a separating funnel. The ester-containing layer is dried (often using anhydrous calcium chloride) and then distilled. The ester is collected at its boiling temperature. This reaction is also described in the alcohols and phenols section, 4.3.

$$CH_3CH_2-C{\overset{O}{\underset{OH}{\big<}}} + CH_3OH \longrightarrow CH_3CH_2-C{\overset{O}{\underset{O-CH_3}{\big<}}} + H_2O$$

Esters often have a characteristic sweet smell and may be liquids or solids at room temperature.

They can be hydrolysed by heating with water but the reaction is slow and does not usually go to completion. If heated with an aqueous alkali (often NaOH), hydrolysis is more rapid and the corresponding alcohol and the salt of the corresponding carboxylic acid are the products. The carboxylic acid itself can be obtained by acidifying the salt (usually with aqueous hydrochloric or sulfuric acids).

$$CH_3CH_2-C{\overset{O}{\underset{O-CH_3}{\big<}}} + NaOH \longrightarrow CH_3CH_2-C{\overset{O}{\underset{O^-Na^+}{\big<}}} + CH_3OH$$

The ester can also be refluxed with an aqueous acid (often sulfuric acid) to produce the corresponding acid and alcohol.

The conversion of carboxylic acids to acid chlorides and their hydrolysis

Acid chlorides are compounds of general formula R-COCl. They differ from the formula of a carboxylic acid by having a chlorine atom in place of the OH group.

There are three common ways to produce acid chlorides from carboxylic acids. The usual method is to react the carboxylic acid with phosphorus(V) chloride, PCl_5. Other routes use phosphorus(III) chloride, PCl_3, or sulfur dichloride oxide, $SOCl_2$.

$$CH_3-C{\overset{O}{\underset{OH}{\big<}}} + PCl_5 \longrightarrow CH_3-C{\overset{O}{\underset{Cl}{\big<}}} + POCl_3 + HCl$$

Acid chlorides are reactive compounds that react vigorously with water giving the corresponding carboxylic acid and hydrogen chloride.

$$CH_3COCl + H_2O \longrightarrow CH_3COOH + HCl$$

quickpire

43 An ester has the formula

$$CH_3(CH_2)_4-C{\overset{O}{\underset{O-CH_2CH_3}{\big<}}}$$

State the names of the alcohol and the acid that could be used to produce this ester.

quickpire

44 Oil of wintergreen contains the ester whose formula is:

Give the molecular formula of this ester.

quickpire

45 Two moles of ethanoic acid react with an excess of PCl_5 to give an 85% yield of ethanoyl chloride. Calculate the mass of ethanoyl chloride that is produced.
[M_r of ethanoyl chloride is 78.5]

Grade boost

Nitriles can be tricky to
name. It is important to
remember that the carbon of
the cyanide group is included
as part of the longest carbon
chain when you name the
compound.

quickfire

㊻ Name the nitrile that has
the formula:
$CH_3CH(CH_3)CH_2CN$

quickfire

㊼ You are given a sample of
bromomethane. Your task
is to produce ethylamine
from it in just two stages.
State the reagents and any
essential conditions for
each stage.

Conversion of carboxylic acids to amides and nitriles

When a carboxylic acid is neutralised by ammonia, the ammonium salt of the
acid is produced.

$$CH_3COOH + NH_3 \longrightarrow CH_3COO^- NH_4^+$$
$$\text{ammonium ethanoate}$$

If the ammonium salt is then heated, water is lost and an amide is formed.

$$CH_3 - COO^-NH_4^+ \xrightarrow{-H_2O} CH_3 - C\overset{\displaystyle O}{\underset{\displaystyle NH_2}{\diagup}}$$

The amide can be strongly heated with a dehydrating agent (such as
phosphorus(V) oxide, P_4O_{10}) when more water is lost, giving a nitrile.

$$CH_3 - C\overset{\displaystyle O}{\underset{\displaystyle NH_2}{\diagup}} \xrightarrow{-H_2O} CH_3 - C \equiv N$$

Formation of nitriles from halogenoalkanes

Nitriles are formed by the reaction of a halogenoalkane and potassium
cyanide, using ethanol as a solvent.

$$CH_3CH_2CH_2Br + KCN \longrightarrow CH_3CH_2CH_2CN + KBr$$

This **nucleophilic** substitution reaction results in the formation of a
compound with an additional C-C bond ('going up the homologous series').

Formation of hydroxynitriles from aldehydes and ketones

Hydroxynitriles can be made by the reaction of hydrogen cyanide with
aldehydes and ketones. This reaction has been discussed in section 4.4.

Hydrolysis of nitriles and amides

If a nitrile or an amide is warmed with dilute sulfuric acid, **hydrolysis** occurs,
giving the carboxylic acid.

$$CH_3 - C \equiv N \xrightarrow{H^+/H_2O} CH_3 - C\overset{\displaystyle O}{\underset{\displaystyle NH_2}{\diagup}} \xrightarrow{H^+/H_2O} CH_3 - C\overset{\displaystyle O}{\underset{\displaystyle OH}{\diagup}}$$

The reduction of a nitrile

A nitrile is reduced by lithium tetrahydridoaluminate(III) (dissolved in
ethoxyethane) producing an amine. This is an example of an addition
reaction, as hydrogen is added across the carbon to nitrogen triple bond.

$$CH_3 - C \equiv N \xrightarrow{4[H]} CH_3 - CH_2 - NH_2$$

4.6 Amines

Aliphatic amines can be made by a substitution reaction from a halogenoalkane, whereas aromatic amines cannot be made this way in the laboratory, but are made by the reduction of nitrobenzenes.

Formation of primary aliphatic amines from halogenoalkanes and nitriles

The reaction of a halogenoalkane with an excess of ammonia, dissolved in ethanol is an example of nucleophilic substitution and produces an aliphatic amine. The other product is a hydrogen halide, which reacts with the excess of ammonia present.

$$CH_3CH_2CH_2CH_2Br + 2NH_3 \longrightarrow CH_3CH_2CH_2CH_2NH_2 + NH_4Br$$

An amine can also be produced by the reduction of a nitrile. The reducing agent used can be lithium tetrahydridoaluminate(III), dissolved in the solvent ethoxyethane. This reaction is also described in section 4.5.

$$CH_3CH_2 - C \equiv N \xrightarrow{4[H]} CH_3CH_2 - CH_2 - NH_2$$

Formation of aromatic primary amines from nitrobenzenes

Halogenobenzenes such as chlorobenzene are not susceptible to attack by nucleophiles such as ammonia and another method is used to produce a primary aromatic amine. The usual method is to heat a nitro compound with a suitable reducing agent, such as tin metal and concentrated hydrochloric acid (shown as [H] in the equation below). Tin is the traditional metal used in small laboratory preparations of primary aromatic amines but this is an expensive metal and commercially, more economical reducing agents tend to be used.

$$+ \ 6 \ [H] \longrightarrow + \ 2H_2O$$

The basicity of amines

The nitrogen atom in the amine group has a lone pair of electrons. These can act as a base by forming a co-ordinate bond with a hydrogen ion. For example, methylamine reacts with hydrochloric acid to give the salt methylammonium chloride.

$$CH_3NH_2 + HCl \longrightarrow CH_3NH_3{}^+Cl^-$$

As a result, an aqueous solution of an amine has a pH of greater than 7 and will turn Universal Indicator to a blue colour. Only 'smaller' amines are soluble in water but 'all' amines react as bases by being proton acceptors / electron pair donors.

Key Term

Ethanoylation = substitution by an ethanoyl group.

Ethanoylation of primary amines

The nitrogen lone pair in the NH_2 group of amines enables them to react as nucleophiles. As a result, they can attack relatively $\delta+$ sites in molecules such as the carbonyl carbon atom in ethanoyl chloride. For example, phenylamine can react with ethanoyl chloride to give a substituted amide.

The product is derived from ethanamide, CH_3CONH_2, with one of the hydrogen atoms of the NH_2 group substituted by a phenyl, C_6H_5, group. Since the phenyl group is bonded directly to the nitrogen atom it is named N-phenylethanamide

Grade boost

You should know that amines can have reactions where the nitrogen atom is lost – as in the reaction of an aliphatic amine with cold nitric(III) acid. You should also know that there are reactions where the nitrogen atom of the amines is retained – as in the formation of azo dyes from primary aromatic amines.

Reaction of primary amines with cold nitric(III) acid

Nitric (III) acid (nitrous acid), HNO_2, is not stable enough to be stored at room temperature. Instead, it is made in the reaction between sodium nitrate(III) (sodium nitrite) and an acid, such as dilute hydrochloric acid and used as it is formed.

When an aliphatic amine reacts with nitric(III) acid at room temperature the products are an alcohol, water and nitrogen gas, which is seen as colourless bubbles in the reaction mixture.

$$CH_3CH_2CH_2NH_2 + HNO_2 \longrightarrow CH_3CH_2CH_2OH + N_2 + H_2O$$
$$\text{propylamine} \qquad\qquad\qquad \text{propan-1-ol}$$

However, when an aromatic amine is used and the temperature is reduced to around 5°C an intermediate diazonium compound is produced in the solution:

benzenediazonium chloride

These diazonium compounds are very reactive and have many useful reactions. The diazonium compounds formed in this way are only stable at lower temperatures. If the mixture is allowed to warm to room temperature and above, decomposition occurs. A phenol, nitrogen gas and a dilute acid are the main products. This is a similar overall process to the reaction of an aliphatic primary amine with nitric(III) acid.

quickfire

㊿ An excess of nitric(III) acid reacted with 0.15 mole of ethylamine. A 60% yield by mass of ethanol was produced. Calculate the mass of ethanol that was formed.

Coupling reactions of benzenediazonium compounds with phenols and aromatic amines

A diazonium compound will react with an aromatic amine giving an azo dye that contains the –N=N- group which is linking the two benzene rings together.

$$\text{Ph–}N_2^+Cl^- + \text{Ph–}NH_2 \xrightarrow{5°C} \text{Ph–}N=N\text{–Ph–}NH_2$$

4-(phenylazo)phenylamine

The benzenediazonium ion is a weak electrophile and will react at points in the benzene ring where the position has been activated (increased electron density) by the presence of an OH or NH_2 group directly bonded to the ring, i.e. phenols and primary amines.

This process is called a coupling reaction and usually results in the loss of a small molecule.

Methyl orange is an azo dye used in acid-base titrations. It can be made by the following reaction:

$$HO_3S\text{–Ph–}N_2^+Cl^- + \text{Ph–}N(CH_3)_2 \longrightarrow HO_3S\text{–Ph–}N=N\text{–Ph–}N(CH_3)_2 + HCl$$

Coupling also occurs with phenols. 4-(Phenylazo)phenol is produced by reacting together benzenediazonium chloride with phenol in an alkaline solution below 10°C.

$$\text{Ph–}N_2^+Cl^- + \text{Ph–}OH \xrightarrow[\text{solution}]{\substack{5°C \\ \text{alkaline}}} \text{Ph–}N=N\text{–Ph–}OH$$

4-(phenylazo) phenol

Other aromatic systems can also couple with benzenediazonium compounds to give azo dyes. A common example of this is the coupling of benzenediazonium chloride with naphthalen-2-ol in alkaline solution to give the red dye 1-(phenylazo)naphthalen-2-ol. This red dye has the common name Sudan 1. Some azo dyes have uses in the food industry but the use of Sudan 1 for this purpose is banned in the UK.

The role of the –N=N– chromophore in azo dyes

Many organic compounds are colourless liquids or white solids. These materials absorb energy in the ultraviolet region of the electromagnetic spectrum. However, our eyes are not sensitive to the ultraviolet region and so we see these compounds as colourless, or white if they are solids. Some organic compounds contain groups of atoms or a series of groups that are responsible for the compound being coloured. Such groups are called chromophores. Often the presence of a single group is not able to produce colour by itself and several groups are necessary for us to see the compound as coloured. Azo dyes are coloured materials as they have the –N=N- group bonded directly to carbon atoms of benzene rings.

Grade boost

The formation of an azo dye from a benzenediazonium compound and a **phenol** needs to be carried out in **alkaline** solution.

quickfire

⑤① Give the **molecular** formula of 4-(phenylazo)phenylamine whose structure is shown in the main text.

quickfire

⑤② One of the simplest azo dyes is the orange-red dye azobenzene.

$$\text{Ph–}N=N\text{–Ph}$$

Calculate the relative molecular mass of azobenzene.

Key Term

Conjugation = a repeating pattern of single and double bonds between carbon atoms.

Origin of colour in terms of the wavelengths of visible light absorbed

White light contains the full spectrum of colours in the visible region of the electromagnetic spectrum. The wavelengths of visible light range from the shorter wavelength violet at about 400 nm (4.00×10^{-7} m), to the longer wavelength red at about 700 nm (7.00×10^{-7} m).

| 4.00 | | 5.00 | | 6.00 | | 7.00 | $\times 10^{-7}$ m |
| violet | blue | green | yellow | orange | | red | |

It is important to realise that both energy and frequency decrease going from the ultraviolet, through the visible region to the infrared region. Thus blue light is of a higher energy than red light. As frequency gets smaller and therefore wavelength increases, blue light must have a shorter wavelength than red light.

ultraviolet ————— visible (blue, red) ————→ wavelength increasing
←————— infrared ————— frequency increasing

Most coloured organic compounds are absorbing light in the visible region of the electromagnetic spectrum. The colour that we see is the colour that is not being absorbed. In spring we see bluebells. Their flowers are absorbing light at the red end of the spectrum, leaving blue, which is the colour that we see. Many coloured organic compounds contain groups that have a double bond (e.g. C=C, C=O or N=N), generally more than one and often in an alternating pattern of double and single bonds (called **conjugation**).

Some examples are shown below.

ethanedial
yellow

nitrobenzene
yellow

1,2-benzoquinone red

1,2-diphenylethanedione yellow

Here is the formula and the visible spectrum of the orange compound β-carotene, found in carrots and a commonly used, and safe, food colouring agent.

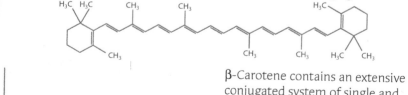

β-Carotene contains an extensive conjugated system of single and double carbon-to-carbon bonds. Since its absorption maximum is at about 480 nm, it absorbs blue light and is seen as orange (in white light).

absorptionn

450   500   550   600   650   700
wavelength/nm

quickfire

㊤ Chlorophyll is responsible for the green colour in leaves. What colours must it be absorbing in sunlight?

quickfire

㊥ Gareth says that a red rose flower appears black when seen in blue light. Explain why he is correct.

quickfire

㊦ A biological stain has an absorption maximum at 510 nm.

State its colour, giving reasons for your answer.

4.7 Amino acids, peptides and proteins

General formula and classification of amino acids

α-Amino acids are carboxylic acids that have an $-NH_2$ group bonded to the carbon atom next to the acid group. The two most common amino acids are aminoethanoic acid (glycine) and 2-aminopropanoic acid (alanine):

$$
\begin{array}{cc}
\overset{\displaystyle NH_2}{\underset{\displaystyle H}{H-\overset{|}{\underset{|}{C}}-COOH}} &
\overset{\displaystyle H\ \ NH_2}{\underset{\displaystyle H\ \ H}{H-\overset{|}{\underset{|}{C}}-\overset{|}{\underset{|}{C}}-COOH}}
\end{array}
$$

aminoethanoic acid   2-aminopropanoic acid
(glycine)   (alanine)

You need to be aware that all α-amino acids, apart from glycine, contain a chiral centre and are therefore optically active. Amino acids have basic ($-NH_2$) and acidic ($-COOH$) groups. They can exist as zwitterions, where a proton is transferred from the acid group to the basic $-NH_2$ group. The zwitterion form of glycine is $H_3N^+CH_2COO^-$.

These zwitterions are ionic and the strong attractive forces between positive and negative charges mean that α-amino acids have higher melting temperatures than expected if they existed as simple covalent molecules. The ionic nature of these compounds means that they are freely soluble in water.

The amphoteric nature of α-amino acids

When α-amino acids are dissolved in acidic or alkaline solutions they can lose or gain a proton respectively. As a result, α-amino acids are amphoteric substances. When they react with an acid they are reacting as bases and when they react with an alkali they are acting as acids.

$$
\overset{\displaystyle NH_2}{\underset{\displaystyle H}{H-\overset{|}{\underset{|}{C}}-COO^-}}
\xleftarrow[\text{solution}]{\text{basic}}
\overset{\displaystyle {}^+NH_3}{\underset{\displaystyle H}{H-\overset{|}{\underset{|}{C}}-COO^-}}
\xrightarrow[\text{solution}]{\text{acidic}}
\overset{\displaystyle {}^+NH_3}{\underset{\displaystyle H}{H-\overset{|}{\underset{|}{C}}-COOH}}
$$

The formation of dipeptides

α-Amino acids can react together to form dipeptides that contain the peptide linkage. A molecule of water is lost when dipeptides are formed.

$$
\overset{\displaystyle H\ \ O}{\underset{}{-\overset{|}{N}-\overset{\|}{C}-}}
$$

Grade boost

If you are asked to write the displayed formula of a dipeptide or part of a polyamide molecule, make sure that you clearly show the structure of the peptide linkage – giving all the bonds.

$$
\overset{\displaystyle H\ \ O}{-\overset{|}{N}-\overset{\|}{C}-} \quad \text{or} \quad \overset{\displaystyle O}{\underset{\displaystyle H}{-N-\overset{\|}{C}-}}
$$

Even if you are giving a structural formula, where all the bonds may not be needed, it is risky to write the peptide linkage as $-NHCO-$. Make sure too, that you do not give the formula of the same dipeptide twice, just written differently!

quickfire

56. Give the names of the two amino acids that combine together to give the dipeptide below.

$$
CH_3CH_2-\overset{\displaystyle COOH}{\underset{\displaystyle H}{\overset{|}{C}}}-\overset{\displaystyle O}{\underset{\displaystyle H}{\overset{\|}{N}}}-\overset{\displaystyle H}{\underset{\displaystyle CH_2CH_2CH_3}{\overset{|}{C}}}-NH_2
$$

quickfire

57. Give the displayed formula of an α-amino acid whose molecules contain four carbon atoms.

quickfire

(58) In the brewing industry glucose molecules are broken down by enzymes from yeast. A molecule of glucose gives 2 molecules each of carbon dioxide and ethanol. Deduce the molecular formula of glucose.

Grade boost

You should know why enzymes are very specific in their reactions when they are compared with catalysts met with in 'ordinary' chemical reactions.

Polypeptides and proteins

This process of peptide formation by the elimination of water molecules (condensation) can continue to form larger molecules (polypeptides) and can then lead on to the formation of proteins. You will need to know a little about the structure of proteins.

Primary structure

This is the sequence of amino acids in the chain. There are twenty amino acids that can make up polypeptide chains. From these there are 400 different dipeptides and 8000 possible tripeptides. A long chain of amino acid fragments means that there are a huge number of possible combinations.

Secondary structure

This is concerned with how the amino acid chains are arranged. There are two common arrangements. In an α-helix the polypeptide chain is coiled into a spiral and its shape is maintained by hydrogen bonding. The other common arrangement is as a β-pleated sheet where the N-H and O-H groups are in different chains.

Tertiary structure

The tertiary structure of a protein is concerned with the way in which the protein chain is folded. Fibrous proteins have a very long chain length and this type of protein tends to be insoluble in water. Another type is the globular protein. These are roughly spherical in shape. Many of these are water soluble or colloidal.

Polyamides

We generally assume that these materials are 'man made' rather than naturally occurring. Polyamides also contain peptide linkages and include nylon. Polyamides are seen in more detail in section 4.8.

The role of proteins in living systems

Enzymes are compounds that catalyse chemical reactions. They can be described as macromolecular biological catalysts and evidence shows that they catalyse over 5000 biochemical reactions. Most enzymes are proteins and are specific in their action because of their unique 3-dimensional structures. The role of enzymes in the body is essential to maintain life, otherwise many reactions would be rather slow! Amylase (present in saliva) catalyses the hydrolysis of starch into sugars. In the brewing industry enzymes such as amylases, glucanases and proteases are responsible for hydrolysing polysaccharides and some proteins to smaller molecules.

4.8 Organic synthesis and analysis

Synthesis of organic compounds by a sequence of reactions

Organic chemists sometimes need a sequence of reactions to be able to produce a required compound from a particular starting material. Questions on this topic have often proved difficult for candidates as they need to know a large variety of reactions and to be able to associate the relevant ones together in the correct order. These questions are sometimes combined with the calculation of percentage yields. This is an important consideration if a product is to be made commercially and there are several ways in which it can be made. This topic is perhaps revised by looking at some specific examples.

Example 1

Study the sequence below and give the reagents needed at each stage and any essential conditions:

$$CH_4 \xrightarrow{①} CH_3Cl \xrightarrow{②} CH_3OH \xrightarrow{③} HCOOH$$

In stage 1 substitution has occurred giving chloromethane. This is a radical reaction and **chlorine gas** is needed in the presence of **sunlight**. In stage 2, substitution has again occurred, but this time it is nucleophilic substitution, and methanol is produced by **heating** chloromethane with **aqueous sodium hydroxide**.

Finally, in stage 3, the oxidation of an alcohol to a carboxylic acid is occurring. As we have seen previously, the alcohol can be oxidised by **heating** it with an **acidified solution of potassium dichromate**.

Example 2

a Study the sequence below and state the names of reagents R and S.

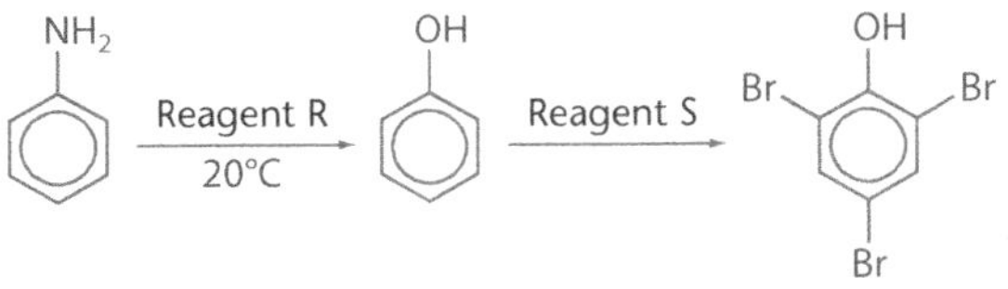

At 20°C phenylamine reacts with **nitrous acid (or sodium nitrite and hydrochloric acid)** (reagent R) to produce phenol. When phenol is treated with **aqueous bromine** (reagent S) a white precipitate of 2,4,6-tribromophenol is produced.

b In an experiment 18.6 g of phenylamine (M_r 93.0) produced 26.5 g of 2,4,6-tribromophenol (M_r 331). Calculate the **percentage yield** of 2,4,6-tribromophenol.

1 Number of moles of phenylamine = 18.8/93 = 0.20

2 Number of moles of 2,4,6-tribromophenol = 26.5/331 = 0.080

3 The equation shows that 1 mole of phenylamine should give 1 mole of 2,4,6-tribromophenol

4 % Yield = actual yield × 100/theoretical yield = 0.080 × 100 / 0.20 = 40

Key Term

Radical = a species with an unpaired electron. This could be an atom, e.g. $Cl^•$ or a molecular species e.g. $^•CH_3$.

Grade boost

It is essential in percentage calculations that you consider the mole ratio of the starting and required materials. Failure to do this will mean the wrong answer and the loss of a valuable mark.

quickfire

(59) Propanone is converted to propene in a two-stage reaction. State the name of the reagents needed at each stage.

Key Terms

Percentage yield =

$$\frac{\text{actual yield}}{\text{theoretical yield}} \times 100$$

Alkylation = the introduction of an alkyl group, e.g. methyl or ethyl into the molecule. This is often met with when alkylating aromatic compounds, e.g. methylbenzene from benzene.

quickpire

⑥⓪ Ethene is converted to ethanoic acid in a two stage reaction. State the name of the reagents needed at each stage.

quickpire

⑥① A compound X reacts with potassium cyanide to give a new compound Y, which then reacts with lithium tetrahydridoaluminate(III) to give ethylamine. State the names of compounds X and Y.

Example 3

Study the sequence below and name the reagents (and catalyst where appropriate) used at each stage.

Stage 1 is the **alkylation** of benzene. To introduce alkyl groups we use the Friedel-Crafts reaction. Reagent E is a halogenoalkane, generally chloromethane would be used (sometimes bromomethane is preferred as chloromethane is a gas and the bromo compound is a liquid). The reaction needs a catalyst. The preferred catalyst (Catalyst F), is aluminium chloride, although iron(III) chloride can be used. The next stage of this reaction is the oxidation of a methyl side chain to a carboxylic acid. This oxidation needs fairly drastic conditions. The preferred oxidising agent (Reagent G) is potassium manganate(VII) (or permanganate) used in alkaline solution. The mixture needs to be refluxed for some time. The product of the reaction will be sodium benzenecarboxylate (benzoate) and this needs to be acidified by adding an excess of aqueous hydrochloric acid to the mixture. The next stage is the esterification of the carboxylic acid to give methyl benzenecarboxylate (benzoate). This esterification is carried out by refluxing the acid with methanol (Reagent H) in the presence of a little concentrated sulfuric acid as catalyst. The final stage is the nitration of this ester to form methyl 4-nitrobenzenecarboxylate (methyl 4-nitrobenzoate). The nitration of benzene to give nitrobenzene needs 'nitrating mixture'. This is a mixture of concentrated sulfuric and nitric acids. The nitration of methyl benzenecarboxylate needs the same mixture of acids (Reagent J). Strictly the question should ask you to **suggest** Reagent J as the nitration of this ester is not mentioned in the specification. However, you should be aware that aromatic nitrations, at this level, all use this same 'nitrating mixture'.

The principles of the techniques of manipulation and purification

Many organic reactions do not go to completion and other products may also be formed. An important part of any organic preparation is the separation and purification of the products. Sometimes the products may be **miscible** with each other (as seen in the preparation of simple esters from an alcohol and a carboxylic acid). Sometimes the products may be immiscible or present in solution, or are produced as a solid. Each of these situations needs a different method of separation and purification.

> **Key Term**
>
> **Miscible** liquids are completely soluble in each other at all concentrations. Examples of this include ethanol and water and benzene and methylbenzene.

Separating miscible liquids

Distillation can be used to separate miscible liquids. If their boiling temperatures are close (perhaps within 20°C of each other), then a fractioning column is also used to help separate the liquids. Distillation can also be used to separate a volatile liquid from other substances in the mixture that are not volatile. A familiar example of a process involving fractional distillation is the primary separation of the components of crude oil (petroleum). The preparation of ethanol by the fermentation of sugars also involves fractional distillation, although complete separation of ethanol from the water present is not easy.

If the liquids to be separated have high boiling temperatures (perhaps >180°C) they can be distilled under reduced pressure (vacuum distillation), which will reduce the boiling temperature. This has advantages if there is a danger of decomposition of the liquids at higher temperatures.

> **Grade boost**
>
> If you are describing (or even using) a separating funnel to separate immiscible liquids, remember to remove the stopper before running off the liquid – otherwise it will not work too well!

Separating immiscible liquids by steam distillation

This is a very important method that is used in the perfumery industry, where essential oils are separated from plant material by passing steam into the mixture. The essential oil distils over with the steam and is condensed to give an immiscible mixture of the oil and water. This is an invaluable technique as the oil will distil over with the steam even though its boiling point may be considerably greater than 100°C. Although it may be easier to just heat the mixture and distil off the oil directly, this is often impractical as many plant oils decompose when heated at higher temperatures.

Solvent extraction

This technique is used to remove a solute dissolved in one solvent into another solvent where its solubility is much greater. A common procedure is to add an immiscible solvent to an aqueous solution containing the solute. The added solvent extracts most of the solute from the water. The two solvent layers can then be separated by use of a separating funnel. The solvent solvent layer is then dried to remove traces of water.

quickfire

62 You are recrystallizing a solid by using ethanol as a solvent. Describe how you would carry this out so that the danger of fire is avoided.

quickfire

63 A white solid is contaminated with a yellow impurity, making it appear slightly yellow. It is washed with a solvent that will only dissolve the impurity. State two ways by which you could tell that all the impurity had been removed.

quickfire

64 Suggest why a solid whose melting temperature is unknown, should be initially dried at room temperature.

Grade boost

When taking the melting temperature of a solid, it is essential to heat the material slowly first to find the approximate temperature range over which it melts. If you heat too quickly the temperature rises too quickly and a likely result is that the measured melting temperature will appear to be higher than that at which melting actually occurred.

Insoluble solid separation

Filtration is generally used to separate a solid from a liquid. This can be by using a filter paper and funnel. A fluted filter paper works more effectively than a filter paper simply divided into four, as the liquid only passes through one layer of paper and the paper only touches the walls of the funnel at the folds.

Alternatively, the solid can be filtered by vacuum filtration using a Buchner funnel and flask and a water pump attached to the tap. This is generally quicker than the traditional filter paper method. It is necessary to dampen the filter paper before use to make sure that it 'sticks' to the flat bed of the funnel.

Using either method the solid in the filter paper is often washed to remove traces of the solution that may remain. The solid can then be removed from the paper and dried at a temperature below its melting temperature – sometimes at room temperature between filter papers or in a drying oven. It is also possible to separate a solid from a liquid by use of a centrifuge.

If it is the liquid that it is required, then the residue in the filter paper is discarded. On a large scale insoluble material can be removed by metal grids or by filtration through gravel, as is used in the water industry.

Soluble solids from solution

If a solute is needed from its solution it can be obtained from it by crystallisation. Sometimes impurities will colour a solution even though the required material is a white solid. The coloured solution can be boiled with decolourising charcoal to remove the colour and the charcoal removed by filtration, leaving a colourless solution.

The solution is concentrated by boiling and then allowed to cool. If sufficient solvent has boiled off, crystals of the solute will appear when it is cool. If not, the mixture is heated until it is concentrated enough to produce crystals on cooling. The crystals are then filtered off and dried at a suitable temperature. The crystals obtained in this way may not be pure – their purity can be checked by taking the melting temperature or by using a suitable spectroscopic method. If the solid is not pure it can be recrystallized. The essential steps for recrystallization are:

- dissolve the solute in the minimum volume of hot solvent
- filter hot, if necessary, to remove any insoluble impurities
- allow the solution to cool
- filter off the crystals
- wash the solid with an appropriate amount of a suitable solvent.

Using melting temperature as a measure of purity

The melting temperature of a solid is the temperature at which it begins to change to a liquid. For many substances, this temperature ranges over one or two degrees. The melting temperature of impure solids will be lower than the expected value and there will a range of temperatures over which it melts. This variation in melting temperature gives an indication of the purity of a substance.

Distinction between addition polymerisation and condensation

There are two types of polymerisation – addition polymerisation, which you will have met in the first year of this course, and condensation polymerisation.

Addition polymerisation

In this type of polymerisation **alkene** molecules are added together to form a poly(alkene). The conditions used for this polymerisation depend on the starting alkene, but this radical reaction generally needs increased pressures. An increased pressure is needed for the polymerisation of gaseous alkene molecules so that the 'molecules are closer together/the concentration is higher'. A radical initiator (shown below as R-R) is also used – this provides a source of radicals for the initiation stage.

$$R - R \longrightarrow 2R\bullet$$

The equation for the polymerisation of propene is shown below.

$$n\ CH_3CH = CH_2 \longrightarrow \begin{bmatrix} CH_3 & H \\ | & | \\ C & - C \\ | & | \\ H & H \end{bmatrix}$$

In addition polymerisation, a compound with a carbon-to-carbon double bond produces a polymer where no double bonds are present. The resulting polymer can have varying physical properties, e.g. hardness, softening temperature and tensile strength, depending on the amount of cross-linking between carbon chains and the arrangement of side chain groups. There are no other products (co-products) obtained during addition polymerisation.

Condensation polymerisation

This is a process where molecules react together to form a polymer with the elimination of a small molecule, such as water. The starting compounds contain two functional groups (often OH, NH_2, or COOH), usually bonded to the two end carbon atoms.)

Grade boost

To obtain the formula of the repeating section of an addition polymer, place the carbon-to-carbon double bond horizontally and all the attached atoms/groups vertically. Make the double bond into a single bond and place all of the 'structure' into a box with the horizontal bonds 'sticking' out of the box.

quicKfire

(65) Use the information in the grade boost above to give the displayed formula of the repeating section of the addition polymer obtained from 2-chlorobut-1-ene.

quicKfire

(66) Write the displayed formula and name the alkene that produces the polymer below.

$$\begin{bmatrix} Br & H \\ | & | \\ C & - C \\ | & | \\ H & Cl \end{bmatrix}_n$$

How polyesters and polyamides are formed

Polyesters

Although there are many polyesters, the specification suggests that we should concentrate on PET. The name PET comes from its older chemical name 'polyethyleneterephthalate'. PET can be made from ethane-1,2-diol and benzene-1,4-dicarboxylic acid.

Grade boost

Always remember that, to produce a condensation polymer, two different compounds are generally needed, both of which contain two terminal functional groups. Alternatively, one compound with two different functional groups can be used, e.g. $H_2N(CH_2)_3COOH$.

Polyamides

These have already been mentioned in the section on α-amino acids and proteins. You are required to know that they are made by the reaction of a diamine and a dicarboxylic acid. A typical **polyamide** is 'nylon'. There are several different polyamides that are described as 'nylon'. The number in the nylon 'name' tells us the number of carbon atoms in each molecule of the starting material. For example Nylon 6,6 is made from hexane-1,6-diamine and hexane-1,6-dioic acid, both of which contain six carbon atoms in their carbon chains.

$$n \; H_2N(CH_2)_6NH_2 \quad + \quad n \; HOOC(CH_2)_4COOH$$

Nylon 6 is slightly more unusual in that it only uses one starting compound, 6-aminohexanoic acid. This compound contains both the $-NH_2$ and the $-COOH$ groups in the same molecule.

In industry, many polyamides are made using more readily available (and cheaper) starting materials. Our study of polyamides is limited to the details outlined above, however.

When a polyamide is made from two different starting materials then the peptide linkage in the polymer is written alternately.

In Nylon 6, however, the peptide linkage is always written the same way.

Nuclear magnetic resonance (NMR) spectra

NMR is concerned with the spin properties of the nucleus. For this specification we are only concerned with the ^1H nucleus (proton) and ^{13}C spectra (the latter has been studied in the first year of this course). An NMR spectrum is obtained when a compound, in a strong magnetic field, is affected by low-energy radio waves. The signal obtained is affected by the environment of the hydrogen atom. For example, the hydrogen proton in ethane, C_2H_6, are all in the same environment, as are all the hydrogen protons in propanone, CH_3COCH_3. However, the single NMR signal for the hydrogen protons in these two compounds will be at different places in the spectrum, as the hydrogen protons in propanone are affected by the C=O group. The usual type of question in the examination requires you to identify various hydrogen protons by use of the provided data sheet. NMR spectra are of two types – low resolution – where only the hydrogen protons bonded to particular atoms are considered and no notice is taken of the influence of neighbouring hydrogen protons (studied in the first year of this course) and **high resolution**. The spectrum shows the low resolution spectrum of ethoxyethane, $CH_3CH_2OCH_2CH_3$. The protons are in a ratio of 4:6 (or 2:3) with signals at ~3.5 and 1.2 ppm respectively.

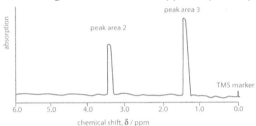

The high resolution spectrum shows that these two signals are again in a ratio of 4:6 but split into a quartet and a triplet respectively.

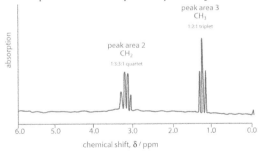

This splitting happens according to the $n - 1$ rule, where n (the number of split peaks in a particular signal) also gives the number of hydrogen protons (atoms) on the neighbouring carbon, oxygen or nitrogen atom.

It is obvious that this splitting pattern can become very complicated if splitting from 'both sides' occurs. For example in 1-chloropropane, $CH_3CH_2CH_2Cl$, the middle CH_2 proton signal will be split to a quartet by the CH_3 hydrogen protons and these will be split again by the CH_2Cl hydrogen protons. The examiners will endeavour to find straightforward NMR spectra without this type of complicated splitting pattern.

» Pointer

If a high resolution NMR spectrum is provided and you see two or more unsplit peaks, then these protons are remote from other protons, e.g. as in chloropropanone $ClCH_2COCH_3$.

▲ Grade boost

If you are given an NMR spectrum and you see a quartet and a triplet, then it is almost certainly due to an ethyl group.

If you are given a high resolution spectrum and you a see a single peak, then this generally means that there are no hydrogen protons bonded to the neighbouring carbon, oxygen or nitrogen atoms.

Grade boost

In thin layer chromatography the R_f value cannot be greater than 1. If you obtain a value greater than 1, then you have the formula upside down! An R_f value of 1 indicates that the compound is moving at the same rate as the solvent. Another solvent should be tried.

quicκɸɪʀe

⑥⑦ You are using GLC. Two compounds appear to have the same retention time. How could you modify the GLC to separate these two components?

quicκɸɪʀe

⑥⑧ A teacher says that when you carry out TLC you should always have the base line above the solvent in the beaker. Why is this?

Chromatography

You will be familiar with paper chromatography and the specification extends this to include thin layer chromatography (TLC), gas chromatography (GC) and high performance liquid chromatography (HPLC). The theory of chromatography is not required but you will need to interpret thin layer chromatograms by using retardation factors (R_f values).

Thin layer chromatography

A TLC plate is essentially an absorbent material mounted on a plastic or glass backing plate. As the solution rises up the plate, the mixture will separate into its individual components. Sometimes two compounds travel up the plate to produce a 'spot' that is unresolved. If this happens, using another solvent may separate the two compounds. The R_f value for compound A can be found using the formula:

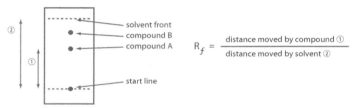

$$R_f = \frac{\text{distance moved by compound } ①}{\text{distance moved by solvent } ②}$$

If compound A is suspected to be a particular compound, then a TLC can be taken of the compound, under the same conditions, and the R_f values compared. If the chromatogram consists of colourless spots then spraying it with a suitable developing agent, or exposing the chromatogram to UV light may produce coloured spots. Each individual compound can be obtained from the spots by 'removing' the spot and dissolving the 'spot' in a suitable solvent, followed by evaporation.

Gas chromatography

The most common type of gas chromatography is gas-liquid chromatography (GLC) where the gaseous mixture is passed 'through' liquid particles supported on an unreactive solid. The gaseous mixture is carried through the column by an inert gas such as helium. The temperature of the column can be adjusted to ensure effective separation. As each compound emerges from the column it is detected and a peak occurs on the chromatogram. The time taken for the compound to emerge from the column is called the retention time. The relative area of each peak is used to give the % of each compound present in the mixture.

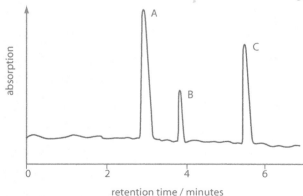

The relative peak areas are shown in the table.

Compound	Relative peak area
A	7.5
B	3.0
C	4.5

The % of compound A = $\dfrac{\text{Relative peak area of compound A} \times 100}{\text{Total peak area}}$

$$= \dfrac{7.5 \times 100}{15} = 50$$

High performance liquid chromatography

This is a useful technique for separating compounds that cannot be easily vaporised, except at high temperatures, when decomposition may occur. The mixture is injected into a **mobile liquid phase** that is under pressure. The chromatogram obtained is similar in appearance to a GLC chromatogram. A typical application would be to analyse drinking chocolate extract for its caffeine and theobromine content.

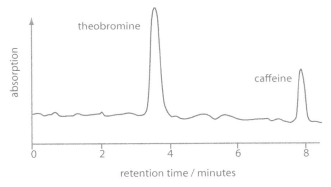

Very often GLC and HPLC columns are linked to other analytical methods. Mixtures are separated using GLC and the separated compounds are fed straight into a mass spectrometer. When the compounds in the mixture are separated using HPLC, the compounds are often fed into ultraviolet/visible spectrophotometers as an aid in compound identification.

>> *Pointer*

You should be aware that HPLC is a useful technique, when run at room temperature for 'larger' molecules that may decompose when heated. One problem that this decomposition would cause is that the chromatogram may show these decomposition products and make interpretation more difficult.

 Grade boost

You should be confident in working out percentages when given in a chromatogram or in table form. Answers should always be given to the same number of significant figures as on the data provided.

Summary: UNIT 4 Organic Chemistry and Analysis

4.1 Stereoisomerism

- This is concerned with the position that atoms and groups take up in space.
- Stereoisomerism includes *E-Z* and optical isomerism.
- Optically active compounds have a chiral centre.

4.2 Aromaticity

- Benzene is stable because of electron delocalisation.
- Many reactions of benzene are electrophilic substitutions.

4.3 Alcohols and phenol

- Alcohols are made by the reduction of aldehydes, ketones and carboxylic acids.
- The hydrolysis of halogenoalkanes gives alcohols.
- Halogenoalkanes are produced from alcohols and hydrogen halides.
- Esters are formed from alcohols and acid chlorides or carboxylic acids.
- Phenols are more acidic than alcohols.
- Phenol decolourises bromine, giving a white precipitate.
- A purple solution is produced when phenol reacts with aqueous iron(III) chloride.

4.4 Aldehydes and ketones

- Only aldehydes give a silver mirror with Tollens' reagent.
- Both give an orange–red precipitate with 2,4-dinitrophenylhydrazine.
- Aldehydes can be further oxidised.
- React with hydrogen cyanide by nucleophilic addition.

4.5 Carboxylic acids and their derivatives

- Reduced by $LiAlH_4$ to aldehydes and primary alcohols.
- Converted to acid chlorides by PCl_5.
- Decarboxylated by soda lime to give alkanes or arenes.

4.6 Amines

- Aliphatic amines are formed from halogenoakanes and ammonia.
- Phenylamine is obtained by the reduction of nitrobenzene.
- Primary aliphatic amines produce alcohols when reacted with nitric(III) acid.
- Primary aromatic amines give diazonium compounds when reacted with nitric(III) acid at low temperatures.
- Azo dyes are formed from diazonium compounds when they react with amines or phenols.
- Chromophores cause colour in organic compounds.
- The colour of organic compounds is due to the colour that is not absorbed.

4.7 Amino acids, peptides and proteins

- α-Amino acids are amphoteric and exist as zwitterions.
- α-Amino acids condense together to give 'peptides' and proteins.
- Proteins have several levels of structure.

4.8 Organic synthesis and analysis

- Condensation polymers include polyamides and polyesters.
- High resolution ^{1}H NMR spectroscopy, (together with other instrumental methods) , are valuable aids in structure determination.
- TLC, HPLC and gas chromatography are used to separate the components from mixtures.

Knowledge and Understanding

Practical Work

The practical work in this course will be assessed by a Practical Examination that carries 30 marks and by a written Practical Methods and Analysis Task that also carries 30 marks. The total marks for Unit 5 count as 10% of the total marks for the A level qualification. Of these 60 marks, around 12 marks are AO1, 30 marks are AO2 and 18 marks are AO3.

Experimental task

This task (the practical examination) will be up to 3 hours in duration and will be taken in the spring term of the A2 year. The specification lists those practical techniques to be experienced by learners, together with a list of suitable practical exercises. The exam board has published a specimen practical exercise to illustrate the type of exercise that might be set in the actual examination. This exercise requires candidates to analyse aspirin tablets for their aspirin content. Obviously in a 3-hour session there are a number of experiments that are not suitable for setting because of time restraints, but that still leaves a range of suitable exercises!

Practical paper

This short paper consists of questions written in a practical context. There is a wide range of topics that could be tested. The specimen paper contains questions on enthalpy of neutralisation, reaction rates and pH changes during neutralisation. An organic question of the 'unlabelled bottles' type is also included. This type of question requires a sound knowledge of organic reactions and a flow chart could be a useful way of answering the question. In this type of question you should be prepared to use instrumental methods, such as IR and NMR spectroscopy as an aid to confirming your results.

Sample question

Three compounds are provided in unlabelled bottles – they are phenylethanone ($C_6H_5COCH_3$), methyl benzenecarboxylate ($C_6H_5COOCH_3$) and benzamide ($C_6H_5CONH_2$). Describe simple chemical methods to decide which one is which.

Sample answer

1) Heat a sample of each compound with aqueous sodium hydroxide. Benzamide, a carboxylic acid amide, will produce ammonia gas, which can be identified by using Universal Indicator paper, turning it blue. The other two compounds will not produce ammonia.

2) Add a sample of the two remaining compounds separately to alkaline iodine solution and warm gently. Phenylethanone contains a methylcarbonyl group ($CH_3C=O$) and this functional group produces a yellow precipitate of triiodomethane with alkaline iodine.

3) The remaining compound must be the ester methyl benzenecarboxylate, which does not give a positive result to either of the two tests.

Note – At room temperature benzamide is a solid – this could be pointed out as an additional point (if known!). The other two compounds are liquids at room temperature.

Exam practice and skills

Aims

To encourage students to:

■ develop their interest and enthusiasm for Chemistry and in further study and careers

■ develop essential knowledge and understanding of different areas of Chemistry and how they are related

■ appreciate how society makes decisions about scientific issues and how science contributes to the success of the economy and of society in general.

A2 Chemistry – a summary of assessment

The assessment at A2 level comprises two written papers, each of 105 minutes. Each paper carries 80 marks. Both are worth 25% of the full A level qualification. In addition there is a practical component of the qualification (Unit 5). This unit comprises two tasks – a practical examination carrying 30 marks and a short written Practical Methods and Analysis task that also carries 30 marks. Unit 5 contributes 10% of the full A level qualification. The A2 level contributes 60% in total to the full A level qualification.

Unit 3 covers Physical and Inorganic Chemistry.

Unit 4 covers Organic Chemistry and Analysis.

Each paper consists of a Section A with short answer questions for 10 marks and a Section B that contains structured and extended answer questions carrying a total of 70 marks. The Quality of Extended Writing (QER) is assessed once in each paper by a question carrying 6 marks.

There are no multiple choice style questions in these papers.

Assessment objectives (AOs) and weightings

Examination questions are written to reflect the AOs described in the specification and you should meet the following AOs in the context of the subject content which is given in detail in the specification.

AO1 covers the knowledge and understanding of all aspects of the subject.

Candidates should demonstrate knowledge and understanding of scientific ideas, processes, techniques and procedures.

AO2 is concerned with the application of acquired knowledge and understanding.

Candidates should apply knowledge and understanding of scientific ideas, processes, techniques and procedures: in theoretical and practical contexts, both when handling qualitative and quantitative data.

AO3 is concerned with the analysis, interpretation and evaluation of both provided and learnt material.

Candidates should analyse, interpret and evaluate scientific information, ideas and evidence and, in relation to issues, be able to make judgements and reach conclusions and to be able to develop and refine practical design and procedures.

Candidates should be aware of **'How Science Works'** and reliably record and communicate observations and measurements.

The weighting for these objectives is the same for both Units 3 and 4 and is

AO1 – 7.2% AO2 – 10.6 AO3 – 7.2%

The weighting for Unit 5 is

AO1 – 2.0% AO2 – 5% AO3 – 3.0%

These figures add up to the full 60% contribution towards the full A level qualification.

Questions that rely on recall only will not exceed 10% in the written papers.

Mathematical skills

These will be assessed throughout both written papers and will have a total weighting of at least 20%. This requirement will be at GCSE Level 2 or above. The skills include arithmetic and numerical computation, handling data, aspects of algebra, geometry, trigonometry and graph work.

Practical work

This essential part of chemistry will be assessed as part of the written papers and also in the Unit 5 practical task. The type of practical work that is required is listed in the specification and will include both qualitative and quantitative analysis, preparations, the measurement of enthalpy changes and reaction rates.

WJEC website

This site, www.wjec.co.uk , should be used to access the specification, specimen assessment materials, past papers and mark schemes and examiners' reports.

Exam tips

Make sure that you read each question carefully. Many marks continue to be lost when candidates answer what they think a question is asking, rather than reading the question all through.

Understand the information

At A2 level, only around 30% of the questions will be based on knowledge and understanding (AO1). About 40% of the questions will be concerned with application of this knowledge and understanding (AO2). In general, the AO2 questions will be more demanding than the AO1 questions. A more detailed response is often required for these AO2 questions. The remaining 30% will be more challenging AO3 questions where you may be required to evaluate your own (and others') work, as well as to refine practical tasks.

Look at the mark allocation

This is an essential part of examination technique. If a question is allocated three marks, then you should ensure that you provide three distinct separate points in your answer.

Understand the instructions

Questions usually begin with key (or command) words. These give a clue as to the depth of response required.

State or give These key words generally need a fairly basic response. Very often these are AO1 questions that are not concerned with any application of known material.

Describe This generally requires a more detailed response than 'state' and may carry two or more marks. This type of question may focus on some learnt theory or on a practical exercise that you have carried out.

Explain This will often carry at least two marks. It requires a higher level of response than 'state' or 'give' and may be an extension of a starting 'state' question.

Compare If you are asked to compare two things, do not simply describe the features of each. The two must be clearly linked together.

Suggest This command word usually indicates that the information required is not direct recall and that there may be a number of acceptable answers. Usually, a 'suggest' requires you to think more widely and to apply knowledge that you have acquired throughout the course.

Tips about structured questions

Structured questions often start with a simple one-word or one-formula answer. The questions are generally devised so that the easier parts are at the beginning and it gets harder further down the question. You should always be prepared to give a diagram or sketch in your answer even if the question does not specifically ask for one. Sometimes a gap is left, rather than lines and this indicates where a diagram should be put. You should ensure that all diagrams are labelled. When giving a formula or a mechanism, be absolutely clear in your answer. Mechanisms involving lone pairs of electrons should have an arrow going from the lone pair that is 'taking part' in the reaction. The correct positioning of lone pairs is important in questions about shapes of molecules/ions and hydrogen bonding.

QER questions

These occur once in each theory paper. The mark scheme shows a list of expected responses (called the indicative content). The examiners note how many of these points have been given and then allocate an overall mark for that question – there is a not a mark for each response – the mark awarded is for the quality of the response. A general outline of the mark range is

5–6 marks

All main features are described and explained and sound evidence is provided for the answer. The account is logical, correct and accurate scientific vocabulary has been used.

3–4 marks

The main features have been described and a simple explanation of how they arise has been given. The use of accurate scientific vocabulary is generally sound.

1–2 marks

Only some of the main features have been described and the account is generally lacking in detail with little explanation given. There is some evidence of the use of correct scientific vocabulary.

0 marks

No attempt has been made or the answer provided is not worthy of credit.

Maximising your performance before and during the exam

- Know the specification.
- Work on past papers.
- Do plenty of calculations.
- Read the question slowly and carefully – do not miss out parts by rushing.
- Try not to leave questions blank – even a guess may be correct, marks are not taken off for wrong or silly answers.
- Give yourself enough time to check your answers.
- Check to see if your numerical answers are sensible and realistic.
- Do not turn over two pages instead of one – it happens every year to someone.

Hints to gain more marks

- Never use the word 'it' without indicating what you mean by 'it'.
- Watch out for command terms in **bold**. For example: **Name** means use the name and **three significant figures** means just that, 86.7 is correct but 87 and 86.72 are incorrect.
- If the question asks for an observation, then give one. For example in a reaction producing carbon dioxide gas, 'bubbles seen' is an observation but 'CO_2 is given off' is not an observation.

Good luck in the examination!

Questions and answers

This part of the guide looks at students answers to examination-style questions through the eyes of an examiner. There is a selection of questions on topics in the A2 specification – one of a high grade standard and one of a lower grade standard in each case. The examiner commentary is designed to show you how marks are gained and lost so that you understand what is required in your answers. Each examination paper will have a question where the 'quality of extended response' is tested in a question (or part question) worth 6 marks. In this question the examiners look for a range of answer points (indicative content) and from the responses to these points award a mark in one of three bands. You will find questions of this type in this question and answer section. In this specification there is more emphasis on numerical answers than in previous papers and also questions will be set that consider the practical work that you will have done throughout the course. The questions set on Unit 4 range across several topics in each question (even though they have a main focus), as is seen in the examination itself.

Your overall grade will depend on the total marks in the examination. Some questions are more difficult than others so it is important that you work out where you can gain the most marks to get the best grade possible. The examiners will decide how many marks are needed for each grade by studying a selection of examination papers that have gained a particular number of marks, and it is common for these candidates to have gained these marks in different ways depending on the topics they find easiest.

Unit 3:   **Physical and Inorganic Chemistry**

page 86	Q1	Reduction and oxidation	(9 marks)
page 87	Q2	Using standard electrode potentials	(6 marks)
page 88	Q3	Redox titration calculations (1)	(7 marks)
page 89	Q4	Redox titration calculations (2)	(7 marks)
page 90	Q5	p-block elements	(6 marks)
page 91	Q6	Group 3	(9 marks)
page 92	Q7	Group 4	(7 marks)
page 93	Q8	Group 7 (1)	(6 marks)
page 94	Q9	Group 7 (2)	(6 marks)
page 95	Q10	Transition metals (1)	(9 marks)
page 96	Q11	Transition metals (2)	(7 marks)
page 97	Q12	Measuring rates of reaction	(10 marks)
page 98	Q13	Rate equations and mechanisms	(7 marks)
page 99	Q14	Enthalpies of formation	(6 marks)
page 100	Q15	Enthalpy and entropy	(6 marks)
page 101	Q16	Using Gibbs free energy	(8 marks)
page 102	Q17	Equilibria	(7 marks)
page 103	Q18	Equilibrium calculations	(6 marks)
page 104	Q19	Acids and pH	(8 marks)
page 105	Q20	Bases and buffers	(8 marks)
page 106	Q21	Titrations and buffers	(6 marks)

Unit 4:   **Organic Chemistry and Analysis**

page 107–108	Q22	Stereoisomerism	(13 marks)
page 109	Q23	Nitration	(7 marks)
page 110–111	Q24	Benzene structure	(6marks)
page 111–112	Q25	Nitromethylbenzenes	(10 marks)
page 113	Q26	Alcohols and phenols	(10 marks)
page 114	Q27	Alcohols and elimination	(10 marks)
page 115	Q28	Ethanedioic acid	(8 marks)
page 116–117	Q29	Acids and esters	(11 marks)
page 117–118	Q30	Preparation of alcohols	(8 marks)
page 118–119	Q31	Diazonium compounds	(9 marks)
page 119–120	Q32	(Chloromethyl)benzene	(8 marks)
page 120–121	Q33	Butane-2,3-dione	(9 marks)
page 122–123	Q34	Structure determination	(9 marks)

Unit 3 Physical and inorganic chemistry

Reduction and oxidation

1 Acidified potassium dichromate is a common oxidising agent, but adding sodium hydroxide solution causes the reaction below:

$$Cr_2O_7{}^{2-} + 2\ OH^- \longrightarrow 2\ CrO_4{}^{2-} + H_2O$$

(i) Give the colour change seen during this reaction. [1]

(ii) Use the oxidation states of chromium to show that this is not a redox reaction. [2]

(iii) The standard electrode potential for acidified potassium dichromate when used as an oxidising agent is +1.33V. Explain what is meant by the term standard electrode potential and describe how this value would be measured. [6]

Tom's answer

(i) orange ⟶ green ✗①

(ii) The oxidation state of Cr in $Cr_2O_7{}^{2-}$ is +12 and in $CrO_4{}^{2-}$ is 2 × +6 = +12. ✗ This isn't a redox reaction because the oxidation states don't change. ✓②

(iii) The standard electrode potential is the voltage you would measure if you connected a half-cell to the standard hydrogen electrode (S.H.E.) under standard conditions (1 mol dm⁻³ concentrations, 1 atm pressure for gases and a temperature of 298 ✓✗). The S.H.E. has a platinum electrode dipping in a solution containing H⁺ (aq) ions, with hydrogen gas bubbled over it. ✓③

Examiner commentary

① The colour change given occurs when dichromate is reduced, and not in this reaction.

② He has doubled the oxidation state, but has gained a mark for his reasoning.

③ This answer is not precise. He receives marks for giving the substances in the S.H.E. and another for giving two standard conditions. He loses a second mark for conditions by missing the K from 298 K, and loses several marks by not discussing the second half-cell or how they are connected.

Tom achieves 3 marks out of 9.

Seren's answer

(i) It turns yellow. ✗ ①

(ii) Chromium in dichromate = +6; chromium in chromate = +6. ✓
This is not a redox reaction because the oxidation state stays the same. ✓ ②

(iii) The standard electrode potential is the value measured on the high-resistance voltmeter when a half-cell is connected to the standard hydrogen electrode. ③

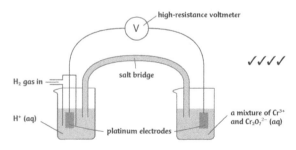

✓✓✓

Examiner commentary

① No mark as the initial colour of the solution is missing.

② Seren gains both marks here.

③ The labelled diagram provides three marks for the substances in each cell, the platinum electrodes. She also gains a mark for the high-resistance voltmeter and salt bridge.

She failed to give standard conditions so doesn't gain these marks.

Seren achieves 6 marks out of 9.

Using standard electrode potentials

2

Dichromate(VI) ions, $Cr_2O_7^{2-}$, react with iron(II) ions in acid solution according to the following equation:

$$Cr_2O_7^{2-} (aq) + 14\ H^+ (aq) + 6\ Fe^{2+} (aq) \longrightarrow 2\ Cr^{3+} (aq) + 7\ H_2O\ (l) + 6\ Fe^{3+} (aq)$$

This reaction can be used as the basis of an electrochemical cell involving the first two of the half-reactions shown below:

	E^{ϑ}/V
$Fe^{3+} (aq) + e^- \rightleftharpoons Fe^{2+} (aq)$	+0.77
$Cr_2O_7^{2-} (aq) + 14\ H^+(aq) + 6e^- \rightleftharpoons 2\ Cr^{3+} (aq) + 7\ H_2O\ (l)$	+1.33
$S_2O_8^{2-} (aq) + 2e^- \rightleftharpoons 2\ SO_4^{2-} (aq)$	+2.01

(i)   Calculate the EMF of the cell.   *[1]*

(ii)   Give the cell diagram that represents this cell.   *[1]*

(iii)   Identify the reducing agent in the reaction above. Give a reason for your answer.   *[2]*

(iv)   Using the standard electrode potentials above, state and explain whether dichromate(VI) ions can oxidise sulfate ions to peroxodisulfate ions, $S_2O_8^{2-} (aq)$.   *[2]*

Tom's answer

(i) EMF = 0.77 – 1.33 = –0.56 V ✗ ①

(ii) $Pt\,|\,Cr_2O_7^{2-}\,|\,Cr^{3+}\,||\,Fe^{2+}\,|\,Fe^{3+}\,|\,Pt$ ✗ ②

(iii) The iron ion is the reducing agent in this case because it has reduced the chromium from oxidation state +6 to +3. ✓ ③

(iv) The dichromate ions are weaker oxidising agents than the peroxodisulfate ions so they cannot oxidise sulfate ions to peroxodisulfate. ✓ ④

Examiner commentary

① The EMF should be positive, so no mark is awarded.

② Tom does not gain credit here as the ions in solution should be separated by a comma not a line. ($Cr_2O_7^{2-}$, Cr^{3+}, and Fe^{2+}, Fe^{3+})

③ He gains a mark for the reason but 'iron ion' is not specific enough to gain a mark.

④ Tom identifies that the reaction cannot occur and gives a reason so he gains a mark. He does not gain the second mark as the question specifies the use of the standard electrode potentials.

Tom achieves 2 marks out of 6.

Seren's answer

(i) EMF = 1.33 – 0.77 = 0.56 V ✓ ①

(ii) $Pt\,|\,Cr_2O_7^{2-},\ Cr^{3+}\,|\,Fe^{2+},\ Fe^{3+}\,|\,Pt$ ✗ ②

(iii) The Fe^{2+} is the reducing agent in this case ✓ because it is being oxidised from +2 to +3, and reducing agents are oxidised as they reduce something else. ✓ ③

(iv) The reaction of dichromate ions with sulfate to make peroxodisulfate would have an EMF of:
EMF = $E_{reduction} – E_{oxidation}$ = 1.33 – 2.01 = –0.68V ✓
A negative EMF means that this reaction is not feasible. ✓ ④

Examiner commentary

① Is correct and gains 1 mark.

② Seren does not gain a mark as she drew the salt bridge as one line.

③ Seren gains 2 marks as she identifies the reducing agent and gives an appropriate reason.

④ Includes a correct identification and reason, and so gains 2 marks.

Seren achieves 5 marks out of 6.

Redox titration calculations (1)

3 Iron(II) sulfate exists as a hydrate, $FeSO_4.xH_2O$. A 1.120 g sample of this hydrated compound was dissolved in distilled water and titrated using acidified potassium dichromate(VI) solution, $K_2Cr_2O_7$. This required 27.20 cm³ of $K_2Cr_2O_7$ solution of concentration 0.020 mol dm⁻³ for complete reaction.

The half-equations for the processes occurring are:

$$Cr_2O_7^{2-} + 14\ H^+ + 6\ e^- \longrightarrow 2\ Cr^{3+} + 7\ H_2O$$

$$Fe^{3+} + e^- \longrightarrow Fe^{2+}$$

(i) Write an **ionic** equation for the reaction between Fe^{2+} ions and $Cr_2O_7^{2-}$ ions in acid solution. [1]

(ii) Calculate the number of moles of Fe^{2+} ions in the sample of iron(II) sulfate used for titration. [2]

(iii) Calculate the relative molecular mass of anhydrous iron(II) sulfate, $FeSO_4$. [1]

(iv) Calculate mass of iron(II) sulfate, $FeSO_4$, present in the original sample of hydrated iron(II) sulfate, $FeSO_4.xH_2O$ and hence calculate the x, the number of water molecules present in each formula unit of hydrated iron(II) sulfate. [3]

Tom's answer

(i) $Cr_2O_7^{2-} + 14H^+ + 6Fe^{3+} \longrightarrow 2Cr^{3+} + 7H_2O + 6Fe^{2+}$ ✗ ①

(ii) Moles $Cr_2O_7^{2-}$ = concentration × volume

$= 0.020 \times 27.20 \div 1000$

$= 5.44 \times 10^{-4}$ moles ✓

Moles $Fe^{2+} = 5.44 \times 10^{-4} \div 6 = 9.07 \times 10^{-5}$ ✗ ②

(iii) $M_r = 55.8 + 32.1 + 16.0 \times 4 = 215.9$ ✓ ③

(iv) Mass $FeSO_4 = 5.44 \times 10^{-4} \times 215.9 = 0.117g$ ✗

Mass water $= 1.120 - 0.117 = 1.003g$ ✓

$x = 1.003/0.117 = 8.5$ ✗ ④

Seren's answer

(i) $Cr_2O_7^{2-} + 14H^+ + 6Fe^{2+} \longrightarrow 2Cr^{3+} + 7H_2O + 6Fe^{3+}$ ✓ ①

(ii) Moles $Cr_2O_7^{2-}$ = concentration × volume

$= 0.020 \times 27.20 \div 1000$

$= 5.44 \times 10^{-4}$ moles ✓

Moles Fe^{2+} $= 5.44 \times 10^{-4} \times 6 = 3.26 \times 10^{-3}$ ✓

(iii) $M_r = 55.8 + 32.1 + (16.0 \times 4) = 215.9$ ✓

(iv) Mass $FeSO_4 = 3.26 \times 10^{-3} \times 215.9 = 0.7g$ ✗ ②

Mass water $= 1.120 - 0.7 = 0.4120g$ ✓

Moles water $= 0.4120 \div 18.02 = 2.286 \times 10^{-2}$

x = moles water ÷ moles $FeSO_4$

$= 2.286 \times 10^{-2} \div 3.26 \times 10^{-3} = 7.017$ ✗ ✓

Examiner commentary

① In part (i) he has mixed up Fe^{2+} and Fe^{3+}.

② The moles of dichromate are correct, but he uses the reacting ratio the wrong way around in part (ii).

③ Part (iii) is correct.

④ In part (iv) he uses the wrong number of moles. If he had used 9.07×10^{-5} correctly he would have gained a method mark. He gains a mark for his working in the second step, but the third is wrong.

Tom achieves 3 marks out of 7.

Examiner commentary

① Parts (i) to (iii) are correct.

② Part (iv) needs the mass of $FeSO_4$ and the value of x. The mass of $FeSO_4$ given is 0.7g and this is too few significant figures. Examiners penalise significant figures where the answer is overtruncated, so if in doubt use more figures rather than fewer.

Seren achieves 6 marks out of 7.

Redox titration calculations (2)

4

(i) Cu^{2+} (aq) ions react with iodide ions to produce copper(I) iodide and iodine, I_2, as the only products. Write an equation for this reaction. *[1]*

(ii) The iodine released can be reduced using sodium thiosulfate solution. Show that 1 $S_2O_3^{2-}$ reacts with the iodine produced by 1 Cu^{2+}. *[2]*

(iii) Bronze contains a significant amount of copper. A 0.98g piece of bronze was dissolved in acid and the solution made up to a volume of 250.0 cm³. Excess potassium iodide was added to a 25.0 cm³ sample of this solution, and the resulting solution titrated with sodium thiosulfate solution. It took exactly 22.75 cm³ of sodium thiosulfate solution of concentration 0.0500 mol dm⁻³ to react with the iodine released. Calculate the mass of copper present in the original piece of bronze, and hence calculate the percentage copper by mass in this alloy. *[4]*

Tom's answer

(i) $Cu^{2+} + 4I^- \longrightarrow CuI_2 + I_2$ ✗

(ii) $S_2O_3^{2-} + I_2 \longrightarrow S_2O_3 + 2I^-$

In this equation 1 $S_2O_3^{2-}$ reacts with 1 I_2 to make 2 I^-. In part (i) 1 copper ion makes 1 I_2. These ratios combine to make it 1:1 overall. ✗ ①

(iii) Moles = 0.05 × 22.75 ÷ 1000 = 1.1 × 10⁻³ ✓
Moles in 250 cm³ = 1.1 × 10⁻³ × 10 = 1.1 × 10⁻² ✓
Mass of Cu = 1.1 × 10⁻² × 63.5 = 0.7g ✗
Percentage by mass = 0.7 ÷ 0.98 × 100 = 74% ✓ ②

Seren's answer

(i) $2Cu^{2+} + 4I^- \longrightarrow 2CuI + I_2$ ✓

(ii) In the equation above $2Cu^{2+} \longrightarrow 1I_2$.
$2S_2O_3^{2-} + I_2 \longrightarrow S_4O_6^{2-} + 2I^-$
In this equation $2S_2O_3^{2-}$ reacts with $1I_2$. ✓
Since $2Cu^{2+} = 1I_2$ and $2S_2O_3^{2-} = 1I_2$, so $2Cu^{2+} = 2S_2O_3^{2-}$ and $1Cu^{2+} = 1S_2O_3^{2-}$ ✓ ①

(iii) Moles $S_2O_3^{2-}$ = 0.05 × 22.75 ÷ 1000 = 1.1375 × 10⁻³ ✓
Moles Cu^{2+} = Moles $S_2O_3^{2-}$ = 1.1375 × 10⁻³ ✗
Mass of Cu = 1.1375 × 10⁻³ × 63.5 = 0.07223g ✓
Percentage by mass = 0.072 ÷ 0.98 × 100 = 7.37% ✓ ②

Examiner commentary

Tom shows a poor understanding of the concepts behind this redox titration but a good understanding of calculations.

① In both parts (i) and (ii) he has misidentified the products of both reactions, leading to incorrect reacting ratios.

② The calculation is correct, and he gains 3 out of the 4 marks available, and only loses a mark for overtruncation of the mass to 0.7g.

Tom achieves 3 marks out of 7.

Examiner commentary

An excellent answer that gains almost full marks.

① The answers for parts (i) and (ii) gain all the marks available.

② Part (iii) gains 3 out of 4 marks, one for calculating the amount of thiosulfate, and one each for the methods in calculating the mass of copper and the percentage by mass. She loses a mark for failing to realise that the amount of moles she has calculated are in 25 cm³ and they need to be converted to the moles in 250 cm³ by multiplying by 10.

Seren achieves 6 marks out of 7.

p-block elements

5 This question discusses the chemistry of some element chlorides of formula XCl_3, commonly called trichlorides.

(a) Aluminium chloride, $AlCl_3$, is considered to be an amphoteric compound.

　(i) State what is meant by the term *amphoteric*. [1]

　(ii) Magnesium chloride contains the non-amphoteric element magnesium. Explain how sodium hydroxide can be used to distinguish between solutions of aluminium chloride and magnesium chloride. [3]

(b) Phosphorus and nitrogen can also form trichlorides, PCl_3 and NCl_3, but phosphorus can also form another chloride, PCl_5. Explain why phosphorus can form phosphorus (V) chloride but nitrogen cannot form a similar chloride. [2]

Tom's answer

(a) (i) Amphoteric compounds have acidic or basic properties. ✗ ①

　(ii) Aluminium chloride solution reacts with sodium hydroxide to give a white precipitate but magnesium chloride is basic so it doesn't react with sodium hydroxide. ✗ ②

(b) Phosphorus can form five bonds because it has d-orbitals in the outer shell. This means that it has enough orbitals to hold the five electron pairs, so it can form five covalent bonds using its five electrons. ✓ ③

Seren's answer

(a) (i) Amphoteric compounds react with both acids and bases. ✓ ①

　(ii) Both aluminium chloride and magnesium chloride solutions react with sodium hydroxide to give a white precipitate. ✓ With excess sodium hydroxide, the aluminium hydroxide precipitate dissolves ✓ but the magnesium one doesn't. ✓ ②

(b) Phosphorus can form five bonds because it has d-orbitals in the outer shell, but nitrogen does not have this d-sub shell. To form a bond an atom needs an orbital with one electron, so five orbitals are needed for five bonds. ✓
Nitrogen has 4 orbitals (1s and 3p) so it is limited to a maximum of four covalent bonds ✓, but phosphorus has 9 orbitals (1s, 3p and 5d) so it can form five bonds with its five electrons. ③

Examiner commentary

Tom loses many marks for carelessness in his answers.

① It is clear that Tom has some idea but by saying acidic OR basic rather than acidic AND basic the answer is not sufficiently clear.

② Tom gains no marks as he displays a common misconception that amphoteric compounds react with sodium hydroxide but non-amphoteric compounds do not.

③ Tom has a good explanation of why phosphorus can form five bonds but does not explain why nitrogen does not. He gains one mark for this.

Tom achieves 1 mark out of 6.

Examiner commentary

① Amphoteric defined clearly.

② Her answer contains all key points (the use of excess sodium hydroxide, the white precipitate formed with both solutions, the precipitate with aluminium dissolving in excess but the other not).

③ Covers the reasons for phosphorus forming 5 bonds and nitrogen not forming 5 bonds.

Seren achieves 6 marks out of 6.

Group 3

6 (a) Aluminium chloride, $AlCl_3$, commonly exists as the dimer Al_2Cl_6.

Draw the structure of the dimer, and explain why the two $AlCl_3$ monomers join together. *[3]*

(b) Both boron nitride, BN, and carbon, C, form hexagonal graphite-type structures.

Explain why:

- BN and C can both adopt a hexagonal structure.
- Both BN and C exhibit lubricating properties.
- C is an electrical conductor but BN is an insulator. *[QER 6]*

Tom's answer

(a)

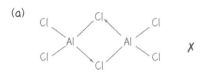

$AlCl_3$ is electron deficient and each chlorine has lone pair of electrons. ✓ ①

(b) Carbon and BN form layers of hexagons with each atom covalently bonded to three others. ✓ The layers have weak forces between them, so the layers can move and cause the materials to be soft and act as lubricants. ✓✓

Carbon and BN both have additional electrons and the ones in graphite are delocalised but the ones in BN are not. ✓ This explains why graphite can conduct and BN cannot. ✗ ②

Examiner commentary

① The arrows point in the wrong direction so he gains no mark. The chlorine lone pairs gains a mark but the Al is electron-deficient not the $AlCl_3$.

② The answer has followed the order of the bullet points to try to address every point required, giving it a clear structure however chemical terminology is not used consistently. The majority of content points are covered with 1 point on the structures, 2 on the explanation of the lubricating properties and 1 on the conductivity. He would need to refer to the electronic structures of both and he would need to discuss how the electrons affect conductivity to cover all points fully.

This is band 2 (3–4 marks) due to content but is presented clearly with enough content to be at the higher end of the band giving 4 marks.

Tom achieves 5 marks out of 9.

Seren's answer

(a)

The aluminium atom is electron-deficient. ✓ The chlorine atoms have lone pairs, so they can form co-ordinate bonds with the aluminium. ✓ ①

(b) Carbon in graphite forms layers of hexagons with each carbon covalently bonded to three others. ✓ The fourth electron is delocalised to form a cloud of electrons between the layers. This allows the graphite to conduct electricity as the electrons can move. ✓ In boron nitride, each boron is covalently bonded to three nitrogen atoms. Each nitrogen has a lone pair, and this is localised on each atom and the electrons can't move, so it can't conduct electricity. ✓ The forces between the layers in both are weak so the layers can slip over each other. ✓✓✗ ②

Examiner commentary

① An excellent answer gaining all 3 marks.

② A clearly presented answer using appropriate terminology. Although she has not followed the order of the bullet points, she has given a good answer covering each of the marking points. The only point she has not included is the fact that the compounds are isoelectronic, which explains the similarities between them.

This suggests the answer would be band 3 (5–6 marks) however the missing marking point limits the answer to 5 marks.

Seren achieves 8 marks out of 9.

Group 4

7 (a) Iron is usually extracted from iron(III) oxide, Fe_2O_3, in a blast furnace according to the equation below:

$$Fe_2O_3 + 3\,CO \longrightarrow 2\,Fe + 3\,CO_2$$

   (i) Explain in terms of oxidation states why carbon monoxide is considered to be the reducing agent in this reaction. [2]

   (ii) Explain why carbon monoxide, CO, can be used as a reducing agent but the corresponding oxide of lead, PbO, cannot. [2]

(b) Describe what is seen when CCl_4 and $SiCl_4$ are added to water separately, giving reasons for any differences. [3]

Tom's answer

(a) (i) The oxidation state of CO is +2 and of CO_2 is +4 ✗. This has gained electrons so it is a reducing agent. ✗ ①

   (ii) Lead is stable in the +2 oxidation state while carbon is stable as a +4 oxidation state ✓. This means that CO will try to convert to CO_2 by reducing something else. ②

(b) When CCl_4 is added to water no reaction happens ✓. When $SiCl_4$ is added to water there are bubbles formed. The difference is because the silicon has d-orbitals. ③

Examiner commentary

① Oxidation states refer to atoms not molecules, so no marks for this. The second part of the answer is totally incorrect.

② A correct statement on oxidation states gains 1 mark, but no explanation so he doesn't gain the second mark.

③ He gains a mark for the observations with CCl_4, but two observations are needed for a mark for $SiCl_4$. The reason given does not compare $SiCl_4$ with CCl_4 so no mark.

Tom achieves 2 marks out of 7.

Seren's answer

(a) (i) In CO carbon has an oxidation state of +2 and in CO_2 it is +4. ✓ Carbon has been oxidised so it must be a reducing agent. ✓ ①

   (ii) Carbon's stable oxidation state is +4. Lead's stable oxidation state is +2 ✓, due to the increase in the inert pair effect on going down the group ✓. This means that PbO is stable and will not want to be oxidised but CO will be oxidised easily. ②

(b) When CCl_4 is added to water it sinks and forms a separate layer ✓. When $SiCl_4$ is added to water, there is an exothermic reaction and bubbles of white fumes of HCl ✓. A white precipitate forms. $SiCl_4$ reacts because it has d-orbitals in its outer shell which water can bond with to start a reaction. Carbon does not have these orbitals so it cannot react. ✓ ③

Examiner commentary

① Oxidation states and explanation gain 2 marks.

② Oxidation states and the inert pair effect gain a further 2 marks.

③ Seren gains 2 marks for the observations, 1 for an observation for CCl_4, and 1 for two observations with $SiCl_4$. The comparison of $SiCl_4$ with CCl_4 clearly gives an explanation for the differences.

Seren achieves 7 marks out of 7.

Group 7 (1)

8 Sodium chloride and sodium iodide are both compounds which contain halide ions.

(a) Silver nitrate solution may be used to differentiate between solutions of sodium chloride and sodium iodide. Give the observations that would be expected in both cases. *[1]*

(b) Both sodium chloride and sodium iodide react with concentrated sulfuric acid. The observations made during both reactions are very different. Discuss the reactions occurring. Your answer should include:

- the observations made during both reactions,
- the identities of any products,
- the reasons for any differences in the reactions that occur. *[5]*

Tom's answer

(i) Iodide gives a yellow precipitate and the chloride gives a white precipitate. ✓ ①

(ii) Sodium chloride reacts with sulfuric acid to produce HCl and NaHSO$_4$. We see white, misty fumes. ✓
When sodium iodide reacts with sulfuric acid this produces HI and NaHSO$_4$. We see this as misty fumes as well. The HI reduces the sulfuric acid producing purple fumes of I$_2$ and a bad egg smell of SO$_2$. ✓✓
The difference is due to the reducing power of iodine, which is stronger than that of chlorine. ✗ ②

Examiner commentary

① This answer gains the mark.

② The observation for the reaction of NaCl is correct and gains a mark. For the reaction of NaI two observations are required for a mark, and misty fumes and purple fumes gain this mark. The bad egg smell is linked to SO$_2$ which is incorrect so no credit is given for this. Apart from SO$_2$ there are three compounds named (HI, HCl, NaHSO$_4$) and this gains 1 mark.

No marks are given for the explanation as he discusses the reducing power of iodine. Iodine is an oxidising agent – iodide is a reducing agent.

Tom achieves 4 marks out of 6.

Seren's answer

(i) Sodium chloride gives a white precipitate, while sodium iodide gives a yellow precipitate. ✓ ①

(ii) When sulfuric acid reacts with sodium chloride it makes HCl and these are released as steamy fumes. ✓ A similar reaction occurs with sodium iodide, releasing HI as steamy fumes. HI is a stronger reducing agent than HCl and can reduce H$_2$SO$_4$ to SO$_2$, S and H$_2$S ✓✓ while HCl cannot do this ✓. We will see purple fumes and a brown solution and black solid formed. ✓ ②

Examiner commentary

① This answer gains the mark.

② The observation for the reaction of NaCl gains a mark, and the observations with NaI gains a mark for two observations. The observations of purple fumes, brown solution and black solid are all due to iodine so only one of these is allowed. Five different products are identified and this gains 2 marks. The reasons for the differences are explained clearly and gain a mark.

Seren achieves 6 marks out of 6.

Group 7 (2)

9 Chlorine reacts with sodium hydroxide in two different ways depending on the conditions used. Discuss the reactions that can occur and the products made. Your answer should show:

- the conditions used for the different reactions,
- the identities of any products, and uses of two chlorine-containing products,
- the equations for any reactions.   *[QER 6]*

Tom's answer

Chlorine reacts with dilute sodium hydroxide solution to do this reaction: ✗

$Cl_2 + 2\,NaOH \longrightarrow NaCl + NaOCl + H_2O$ ✓✓①

The NaCl can be used as table salt and the NaOCl can be used as a bleach. ✓

Chlorine reacts with concentrated sodium hydroxide solution in this reaction:

$1\tfrac{1}{2}\,Cl_2 + 4\,NaOH \longrightarrow 2\,NaCl + NaClO_3 + 2\,H_2O + Na^-$ ✓✗

The NaCl can be used as table salt. ✗②

Examiner commentary

① The conditions given are not sufficient, as he does not refer to temperature.

For the first reaction, the equation is correct and there is further credit for the products. A third mark is awarded for the correct uses for each product.

② For the second reaction, the equation gives the correct products for some credit but it is not balanced and so no further credit given.

The answer covers most (but not all) marking points. These are expressed clearly so this places the answer at the upper end of band 2 (3–4 marks).

Tom achieves 4 marks out of 6.

Seren's answer

When cold, aqueous sodium hydroxide reacts with chlorine it makes NaCl (used as a food preservative) and NaOCl (used as bleach). ✓✓✓. The equation for this is:

$Cl_2 + 2\,NaOH \longrightarrow NaCl + NaOCl + H_2O$ ✓①

Chlorine reacts with hot concentrated sodium hydroxide solution to make NaCl and $NaClO_3$. ✓✓

$Cl_2 + 6\,NaOH \longrightarrow 5\,NaCl + NaClO_3 + 3\,H_2O$ ✓ ②

Examiner commentary

The conditions given for both reactions are complete.

① For the first reaction, the products are correct and the equation is complete and balanced. Credit is awarded for the correct uses for each product.

② For the second reaction the products are correct and the equation is complete and balanced.

The answer covers all the key marking points. These are expressed clearly so this places the answer at the upper end of band 3 (5–6 marks).

Seren achieves 6 marks out of 6.

Transition metals (1)

10 (a) Copper(II) ions can form the following coloured complexes: $[Cu(H_2O)_6]^{2+}$ and $[CuCl_4]^{2-}$.

    (i) State the shape and colour for each complex. [2]
    (ii) Describe the bonding in copper(II) complexes. [2]
    (iii) Explain why the complex $[Cu(H_2O)_6]^{2+}$ is coloured. [3]

  (b) Give the electronic configuration of copper(I) ions, Cu^+, and state why copper(I) compounds are not usually coloured. [2]

Tom's answer

(a) (i) $[Cu(H_2O)_6]^{2+}$ = octahedral, royal blue; ✓
$[CuCl_4]^{2-}$ = tetrahedral, yellow. ✗①

  (ii) Complexes consist of a Cu^{2+} ion surrounded by small molecules called ligands that are bonded to it. ✓✗②

  (iii) The d-orbitals in the transition metal are split into two energy levels, 3 lower and 2 higher. Electrons are promoted from the lower to the higher energy level by absorbing particular colours of light ✓, making the complex coloured. ✗③

(b) The electron configuration of a Cu^+ ion is $1s^2 2s^2 2p^6 3s^2 3p^6 3d^{10}$ ✓. The energy levels are not split so light is not absorbed. ✗④

Examiner commentary

① Tom has the correct shapes and colours except for the colour of the second complex.

② In part (a) (ii) the arrangement of ions and ligands are clear, but the type of bonding present is needed for the second mark.

③ Tom does not give the cause of the d-orbital splitting. He identifies the movement of electrons to higher energy level by absorbing light, but needs to specify that the colour seen is the remaining colours which are not absorbed.

④ He gains a mark for the correct electronic configuration, but the reason is incorrect.

Tom achieves 4 marks out of 9.

Seren's answer

(a) (i) $Cu(H_2O)_6]^{2+}$ = octahedral, pale blue;
$[CuCl_4]^{2-}$ = tetrahedral, green. ✓✓

  (ii) Complexes consist of a Cu^{2+} ion surrounded by small molecules with lone pairs called ligands that form co-ordinate bonds with it. ✓✓

  (iii) When ligands bond to the metal ion, they cause the d-orbitals to split in energy, with 3 lower and 2 higher energy levels. Electrons can move from the lower to the higher level by absorbing the correct amount of energy. This corresponds to a particular frequency of light, which gives the colour of the complex. ✓✓ ①

(b) The electron configuration of a Cu^+ ion is $1s^2 2s^2 2p^6 3s^2 3p^6 3d^{10}$. The d-orbitals are full, so there is no space for electrons to move, and so no frequencies of light are absorbed. ✓✓②

Examiner commentary

① Seren loses 1 mark in part (a). In part (iii) she has failed to indicate that it is the frequencies of light NOT absorbed that give the colour of the complex.

② In part (b), Seren gains both marks for correctly identifying the electronic configuration and the fact that the d-orbitals are full.

Seren achieves 8 marks out of 9.

Transition metals (2)

11 (c) Explain why chromium and copper are considered to be transition elements, but zinc is not. *[1]*

(d) Describe what is seen when excess sodium hydroxide solution is slowly added to a solution of chromium(III) chloride, $CrCl_3$, giving chemical equations for any reactions occurring. *[4]*

(e) Give a common use for a named transition metal or transition metal compound in industry. *[2]*

Tom's answer

(c) Chromium and copper both have partially filled d-orbitals in at least one of their ions, but zinc forms Zn^{2+} which has a full set of d-orbitals. ✓①

(d) On adding sodium hydroxide solution to chromium(III) chloride solution, a grey-green precipitate forms that redissolves in excess sodium hydroxide solution. ✓

$Cr^{3+} + 3\,OH^- \longrightarrow Cr(OH)_3$ ✓②

$Cr(OH)_3 + OH^- \longrightarrow [Cr(OH)_4]^-$ ✗③

(e) Iron is used as a catalyst for the production of ammonia. ✓④

Examiner commentary

① Tom gains the mark for part (c).

② He gains two marks for part (d), as he gives one observation (the grey-green precipitate) and one correct equation. It is important to give the observations throughout to gain the full marks, and this includes the colours of the original solution and the final solution (green in both cases).

③ The second equation given is incorrect as three hydroxide ions need to react to form the correct complex.

④ One mark is awarded for a correct use.

Tom is awarded 4 marks out of 6.

Seren's answer

(c) Chromium and copper both have partially filled d-orbitals but zinc has a full set of d-orbitals. ✗①

(d) Chromium(III) chloride solution is dark green, and when some sodium hydroxide solution is added a grey-green precipitate forms ✓. Adding more sodium hydroxide causes the precipitate to dissolve to form a green solution. ✓

$Cr^{3+} + 3\,OH^- \longrightarrow Cr(OH)_3$ ✓

$Cr(OH)_3 + 3\,OH^- \longrightarrow [Cr(OH)_6]^{3-}$ ✓②

(e) Copper is used in electronics ✓. Cobalt is present in vitamin B-12. ③

Examiner commentary

① Seren doesn't gain a mark for (c) as she doesn't mention ions.

② She gains full marks for part (d), as she gives descriptions of what is observed before adding sodium hydroxide, with a small amount of the solution added and with excess added. Both equations are also correct.

③ Seren lists uses of two different metals, one in industry and one in biology and so gains the mark for the industrial use and the biological one is ignored.

Seren is awarded 5 marks out of 6.

Measuring rates of reaction

12 Nitrogen(V) oxide, N_2O_5, decomposes according to the equation:

$$2 N_2O_5 (g) \longrightarrow 4 NO_2 (g) + O_2 (g)$$
Colourless   brown   colourless

(a) Suggest two ways of measuring the rate of this reaction. *[2]*

(b) Under most conditions the rate of this reaction is given by:

$$Rate = k [N_2O_5]$$

When the concentration of N_2O_5 is 4.00×10^{-3} mol dm^{-3} the rate of the reaction at 350 K was found to be 3.00×10^{-5} mol dm^{-3} s^{-1}.

   (i) Calculate the value of the rate constant to **three** significant figures, giving its unit. *[3]*

   (ii) If the reaction were repeated with an initial concentration of N_2O_5 of 6.00×10^{-3} mol dm^{-3}, calculate the expected value of the rate of reaction. *[1]*

   (iii) A catalyst reduces the activation energy of this reaction from 72 kJ mol^{-1} to 50 kJ mol^{-1}.

      I. State the Arrhenius equation. *[1]*

      II. Calculate the value of the rate constant of the catalysed reaction at 350 K. *[3]*

Tom's answer

(a) The rate could be measured using colorimetry ✗ or by measuring the amount of NO_2 produced. ✗①

(b) (i) $k = Rate \div [N_2O_5] = 3.00 \times 10^{-5} \div 4.00 \times 10^{-3}$
     $= 0.75 \times 10^{-2}$ ✓✗ mol dm^{-3} s^{-1} ✗ ②

  (ii) Because the rate is proportional to concentration, when concentration is multiplied by 1.5 the rate is 4.5×10^{-5} mol dm^{-3}. ✓ ③

  (iii) I. $Ae^{(-E_a/_{RT})}$ ④
     II. $A = k \div e^{(-E_a/_{RT})}$ ⑤ $A = 0.75 \times 10^{-2} \div e^{(-72/_{8.314 \times 350})} = 7.69 \times 10^{-3}$
              $k = 7.69 \times 10^{-3} \div e^{(-50/_{8.314 \times 350})} = 7.56 \times 10^{-3}$ ⑥

Examiner commentary

① To measure rate you need to take a measurement that changes over time – if time is not measured then this will reduce the marks so 'colorimetry' without time is not enough for a mark.

② When significant figures are requested in bold print, then only these are accepted, so he loses a mark for an answer to 2 significant figures.

③ Proportion is a good method for working out rates for first order reactions so gains a mark.

④ This does not gain the mark as the question asks for an equation and so the lack of $k =$ makes the answer incorrect.

⑤ This is a correct rearrangement of the equation and gains one mark.

⑥ The value of the activation energy has not been converted into J from kJ and so the calculation is incorrect, however this is the only error the candidate makes so they gain one out of the two marks available for the calculation.

Tom achieves 4 out of 10 marks.

Seren's answer

(a) Since there is a change in colour we can use colorimetry to measure the colour over time. ✓ The change in the number of molecules of gas can be tracked using pressure measurements at constant volume. ✓①

(b) (i) $k = Rate \div [N_2O_5]$
     $= 3.00 \times 10^{-5} \div 4.00 \times 10^{-3}$
     $= 7.50 \times 10^{-3}$ ✓✓ s^{-1}✓

  (ii) Using the rate equation,
     rate $= 7.50 \times 10^{-3} \times 6.00 \times 10^{-3}$
     $= 4.5 \times 10^{-5}$ mol dm^{-3}. ✓ ②

  (iii) I. $k = Ae^{(-E_a/_{RT})}$ ✓ ③
     II. $A = k \div e^{(-E_a/_{RT})}$ ④
     $A = 0.75 \times 10^{-2} \div e^{(-72000/_{8.314 \times 350})} = 4.18 \times 10^8$
     $k = 4.18 \times 10^8 \times e^{(-50000/_{8.314 \times 350})} = 14.4$ ✓✓✓ ⑤

Examiner commentary

① Two methods are suggested and although time is only mentioned once, this is enough to gain both marks

② Both calculations are correct.

③ This is the correct equation and gains the mark.

④ This is a correct rearrangement of the equation and gains one mark.

⑤ This calculation is correct and gains both marks.

Seren achieves 10 marks out of 10.

Rate equations and mechanisms

13

Hydrogen peroxide (H_2O_2) in solution decomposes to release oxygen gas when in the presence of iodide ions. The equation for this process is:

$$2H_2O_2 \longrightarrow 2H_2O + O_2$$

The reaction was repeated using several different concentrations of hydrogen peroxide and iodide ions. The results of these experiments are given below.

Concentration of H_2O_2 / mol dm^{-3}	Concentration of I$^-$ / mol dm^{-3}	Initial rate / mol dm^{-3} s^{-1}
2.00×10^{-2}	2.00×10^{-3}	4.82×10^7
4.00×10^{-2}	2.00×10^{-3}	9.64×10^7
4.00×10^{-2}	4.00×10^{-3}	1.93×10^8

(a) Calculate the orders of the reaction with respect to H_2O_2 and iodide ions and hence write a rate equation for this reaction. [3]

(b) State the function of the iodide ions in this reaction and explain your reasoning. [2]

(c) Two proposed mechanisms for this reaction are given below as mechanism A and mechanism B. State and explain which of these two mechanisms is consistent with the rate equation you have found in part (a). [2]

Mechanism A	Mechanism B
$H_2O_2 \longrightarrow H^+ + HO_2^-$	$H_2O_2 + I^- \longrightarrow HOI + HO^-$
$HO_2^- + HO_2^- \longrightarrow 2HO^- + O_2$	$HOI + H_2O_2 \longrightarrow H_2O + O_2 + HI$
$H^+ + I^- + HO^- \longrightarrow H_2O + I^-$	$HI + OH^- \longrightarrow H_2O + I^-$
Mechanism A	*Mechanism B*

Tom's answer

(a) Doubling the concentration of H_2O_2 doubles rate so the order is 1. ✓ Doubling the concentration of iodide doesn't double the rate so the order is 0. ✗ ①
Rate = k[H_2O_2] ✓

(b) Iodide is needed for the reaction to occur. ✗ ②

(c) Mechanism A as it only has H_2O_2 in the first step and this is the slowest step. The rate equation only has H_2O_2 in it so it matches. ✓✗ ③

Examiner commentary

① This is correct for H_2O_2 but incorrect for I$^-$; however, the orders are correctly used to produce a rate equation so this gains a mark even though it is not the correct answer.

② This tells us nothing and gains no mark.

③ This answer follows from the rate equation and gives a reason so gains a mark but the reason is insufficient for the second mark.

Tom achieves 3 out of 7 marks.

Seren's answer

(a) H_2O_2 is first order ✓, and iodide is first order ✓, giving a rate equation of:
Rate = k[H_2O_2][I$^-$] ✓ ①

(b) The iodide increases the rate even though it is not part of the overall equation ✓ so the iodide acts as a catalyst ✓.②

(c) Mechanism B as it has one H_2O_2 molecule and one iodide as the reactants in the rate determining step which matches the two compounds in the rate equation, and both of these are first order. ✓✓③

Examiner commentary

① Both orders are calculated correctly, giving an overall rate equation.

② Catalysts will appear in the rate equation but will not appear in the chemical equation so this answer is correct.

③ The correct answer with a full reason gains both marks.

Seren achieves 7 out of 7 marks.

Enthalpies of formation

14 Sodium hydride, NaH, is a solid that reacts with water. The synthesis of the compound from the elements sodium and hydrogen is an exothermic process:

$$Na\ (s) + \tfrac{1}{2} H_2\ (g) \longrightarrow NaH\ (s) \qquad \Delta H^{\theta} = -57\ kJ\ mol^{-1}$$

(a) Give the name of the enthalpy change above. *[1]*

(b) Use the enthalpy change above, and those listed in the table below to calculate the enthalpy of lattice formation for sodium hydride, NaH. *[3]*

Equation	Enthalpy change / kJ mol⁻¹
$Na\ (s) \longrightarrow Na\ (g)$	109
$H_2\ (g) \longrightarrow 2H\ (g)$	436
$Na\ (g) \longrightarrow Na^+\ (g) + e^-$	494
$H\ (g) + e^- \longrightarrow H^-\ (g)$	−72

(c) When NaH is added to water, the following reaction occurs:

$$NaH\ (s) + H_2O\ (l) \longrightarrow NaOH\ (aq) + H_2\ (g)$$

Calculate the number of moles of NaH and hence the volume of hydrogen gas produced under standard conditions when 1.2g of NaH is added to water. *[2]*

[1 mole of gas occupies 24 dm³ under standard conditions]

Tom's answer

(a) Enthalpy of formation of NaH. ✓①

(b) $\Delta H = 109 + 436 + 494 - 72 + \Delta H_{Latt}$ ✗
    $-57 - 109 - 436 - 494 + 72 = \Delta H_{Latt}$ ✓
    $\Delta H_{Latt} = -1024\ kJ\ mol^{-1}$ ✓②

(c) $M_r(NaH) = 23 + 1.01 = 24.01$
    Moles (NaH) = 1.2 ÷ 24.01 = 0.05 ✗
    Volume gas = 0.05 × 24 = 1.2 dm³ ✓③

Examiner commentary

① (a) is correct.
② Tom has not noticed that the equation given for 436 kJ mol⁻¹ involves 2H so this must be halved. He gains the marks available for the remainder of the method.
③ Tom correctly calculates the moles of NaH and the volume of gas, but misses a mark as he has overtruncated the moles of NaH.

Tom achieves 4 out of 6 marks.

Seren's answer

(a) Enthalpy of formation for NaH (s). ✓①

(b) $-57 = 109 + \tfrac{1}{2} \times 436 + 494 - 72 + \Delta H_{Latt}$ ✓
    $-57 - 109 - 218 - 494 + 72 = \Delta H_{Latt}$ ✓
    $\Delta H_{Latt} = -806\ kJ\ mol^{-1}$ ✓②

(c) $M_r(NaH) = 23 + 1.01 = 24.01$
    Moles (NaH) = 1.2 ÷ 24.01 = 0.04998 ✓
    Volume gas = 0.04998 × 24 = 1.20 dm³ ✓③

Examiner commentary

① (a) is correct.
② Seren has worked out the stages that need to be combined to make the overall process, and rearranges the equation correctly to gain full marks.
③ Seren correctly calculates the moles of NaH and uses this to calculate the volume of gas.

Seren achieves 6 out of 6 marks.

Enthalpy and entropy

15

The equation below shows the complete combustion of liquid methanol.

$$CH_3OH (l) + 1\tfrac{1}{2}O_2 (g) \longrightarrow CO_2 (g) + 2 H_2O (l)$$

(a) Use the enthalpy changes of formation listed in the table below to calculate the enthalpy change of this reaction. *[2]*

	Standard enthalpy change of formation / kJ mol^{-1}
CH_3OH (l)	−239
CO_2 (g)	−394
H_2O (l)	−286
O_2 (g)	0

(b) Explain why the enthalpy change of formation of O_2 (g) is zero. *[1]*

(c) (i) The entropy change of this reaction is −81 J K^{-1} mol^{-1}. Use this value to calculate the Gibbs free energy for this reaction at 300 K. *[2]*

   (ii) Explain how the answer to (c)(i) allows us to decide whether the reaction is feasible. *[1]*

Tom's answer

(a) ΔH = products − reactants
      = −394 − 286 − 239 ✗
      = −919 kJ mol^{-1} ✗ ①

(b) The enthalpy of formation is the enthalpy change from the element so it is zero for oxygen. ✗②

(c) (i) ΔG = ΔH − TΔS ✓ = −919 − 300 × −81
        = 23381 kJ mol^{-1} ✗ ③

   (ii) The value is positive so the reaction is not feasible. ✓④

Examiner commentary

① Incorrect as Tom has forgotten to include the factor of two for the two water molecules, and the value for methanol should be positive.

② The details here are insufficient as there is no reference to standard state.

③ He has forgotten to convert the entropy to kJ, so he loses a mark, but gains a mark for a correct expression for ΔG.

④ A mark is awarded as the answer is consistent with the value obtained in part (i)

Tom achieves 2 out of 6 marks.

Seren's answer

(a) ΔH = products − reactants
      = −394 −2 × 286 −(−239) ✓
      = −727 kJ mol^{-1} ✓①

(b) The enthalpy of formation is the enthalpy change when a substance is formed from its elements in their standard states, in this case O_2 (g). Since there is no change the enthalpy change is zero. ✓②

(c) (i) ΔG = ΔH − TΔS✓ = −727000 − 300 × −81
        = −702700 ✗ ③

   (ii) The reaction is feasible. ✗④

Examiner commentary

① Calculated correctly and gains both marks.

② The explanation is full and detailed and so gains the mark.

③ This is correctly calculated; however, the answer given has no units, and this is penalised as we assume kJ mol^{-1} as this is the standard unit for ΔG.

④ This answer gives no explanation so gains no mark.

Seren achieves 4 out of 6 marks.

Using Gibbs free energy

16 When calcium nitrate is heated, the solid decomposes according to the equation below.

$$2 \, Ca(NO_3)_2 \, (s) \longrightarrow 2 \, CaO \, (s) + 4 \, NO_2 \, (g) + O_2 \, (g)$$

(a) The standard enthalpy change, ΔH^θ, for the reaction is 740 kJ mol^{-1}. Use this value and the data in the table to calculate the standard enthalpy of formation, ΔH_f^θ, for calcium nitrate, $Ca(NO_3)_2$. *[2]*

	ΔH_f^θ / kJ mol^{-1}	S^θ / J mol^{-1} K^{-1}
$Ca(NO_3)_2$	?	193
CaO	−635	40
NO_2	34	240
O_2	0	205

(b) Use the values given to calculate the entropy change ΔS^θ for this reaction in J mol^{-1} K^{-1}. *[2]*

(c) State the relationship between Gibbs free energy, enthalpy and entropy. *[1]*

(d) Use the expression for Gibbs free energy to calculate the minimum temperature, in K, required for decomposition of calcium nitrate. *[3]*

Tom's answer

(a) $\Delta H = 2 \times -635 + 4 \times 34 + 0 - 2 \times ?$ ✓
 $740 - 2 \times -635 - 4 \times 34 = 2 \times ?$
 Answer = 937 kJ mol^{-1} ✗ ①

(b) ΔS^θ = products – reactants
 $= 2 \times 40 + 4 \times 240 + 205 - 2 \times 193$ ✓
 $= 654$ J mol^{-1} K^{-1} ✓ ②

(c) $\Delta G = \Delta H - T\Delta S$ ✓ ③

(d) When the reaction is able to happen then ΔG must become negative, and it becomes negative at zero. ✓
 $\Delta G = 740 - T \times 859 = 0$ so $T \times 859 = 740$ ✗
 $T = 740 \div 859 = 0.86 \,°C$ ✗ ④

Examiner commentary

① Tom has the correct idea but makes an error in rearrangement of the equation which loses a mark.

② ③ Both correct.

④ Starts correctly; however, he forgets to convert between J and kJ so both entropy and enthalpy can be used together. He finally gives the answer in the wrong temperature units.

Tom achieves 5 out of 8 marks.

Seren's answer

(a) $740 = (2 \times -635) + (4 \times 34) + 0 - (2 \times \Delta H_f)$ ✓
 $740 - (2 \times -635) - (4 \times 34) = - (2 \times \Delta H_f)$
 $2 \times \Delta H_f = -1874$
 Answer $= -937$ kJ mol^{-1} ✓

(b) $\Delta S^\theta = (2 \times 40) + (4 \times 240) + 205 - (2 \times 193)$ ✓
 $= 654$ J mol^{-1} K^{-1} ✓

(c) $\Delta G = \Delta H - T\Delta S$ ✓

(d) The reaction starts to be feasible when $\Delta G = 0$ so $\Delta H - T\Delta S = 0$ giving $T = \Delta H \div \Delta S$ ✓
 We need to use the same units for ΔH and ΔS so $\Delta H = 740,000$ J mol^{-1}. ✓
 $T = \Delta H \div \Delta S = 740000 \div 859 = 861$ K ✓

Examiner commentary

Seren shows her ability to undertake calculations competently. All of Seren's answers are correct, with all units used correctly.

Seren achieves 8 out of 8 marks.

Equilibria

17 One stage in the production of nitric acid involves the oxidation of ammonia, which is a reversible reaction as shown below.

$$4\,NH_3\,(g) + 5\,O_2\,(g) \rightleftharpoons 4NO\,(g) + 6\,H_2O\,(g)$$

(a) Write the expression for the equilibrium constant, K_p, for this reaction. *[1]*

(b) The values for all the partial pressures are typically given with units of Pa. Give the unit, if any, of K_p for this reaction. *[1]*

(c) A platinum/rhodium catalyst is used in the industrial process. State the effect, if any, of adding a catalyst on the position of this equilibrium. *[1]*

(d) This reaction is usually undertaken under a pressure of 500 kPa. State and explain the effects, if any, of increasing the pressure on the position of equilibrium and the rate of the forward reaction. *[4]*

Tom's answer

(a) $K_p = \dfrac{P_{NO} \times P_{H_2O}}{P_{NH_3} \times P_{O_2}}$ ✗ ①

(b) There will be no units. ✓ ②

(c) Catalysts affect the rate the forward and reverse reactions, so these cancel out. ✗ ③

(d) The reaction is faster at a higher pressure ✓ ✗ and it produces more product. ✗✗ ④

Examiner commentary

① Tom has forgotten the powers so loses the mark.

② This mark is given as the answer follows from the expression given in part (a) even though this is incorrect.

③ This is the correct idea but doesn't answer the question completely so doesn't gain the mark.

④ The effect on rate is correct, but the effect on the equilibrium is not. Neither are explained so this limits the mark available.

Tom achieves 2 out of 7 marks.

Seren's answer

(a) $K_p = \dfrac{P_{NO}^4 \times P_{H_2O}^6}{P_{NH_3}^4 \times P_{O_2}^5}$ ✓ ①

(b) Units will be Pa. ✓ ②

(c) Catalysts affect the rate but not the position of equilibrium. ✓ ③

(d) The reaction is faster at a higher pressure ✓ as the particles collide more ✗. The equilibrium will try to decrease the pressure according to Le Chatelier's principle so it will go to the side with fewer gas molecules, which shifts the equilibrium to the left. ✓✓ ④

Examiner commentary

① ③ Exactly what was expected for the marks.

④ The effect on rate is correct, but the explanation is not sufficient. The effect on the equilibrium is correct with a clear explanation so she gains both marks here.

Seren achieves 6 out of 7 marks.

Equilibrium calculations

18 Nitrogen dioxide, NO_2, exists in dynamic equilibrium with dinitrogen tetroxide, N_2O_4,

$$2NO_2 \text{ (g)} \rightleftharpoons N_2O_4 \text{ (g)} \qquad \Delta H = -57.2 \text{ kJ mol}^{-1}$$

(a) Write an expression for the equilibrium constant, K_p, for this reaction. *[1]*

(b) State and explain the effect of increasing the temperature on the value of K_p. *[2]*

(c) At a temperature of 373 K, the partial pressure of a pure sample of NO_2 was 3.00×10^5 Pa. When the mixture was allowed to reach equilibrium, the partial pressure of the remaining NO_2 was 2.81×10^5 Pa.

Calculate the value of K_p, stating its units. *[3]*

Tom's answer

(a) $K_p = \dfrac{P_{N_2O_4}}{P_{NO_2}^{2}}$ ✓ ①

(b) The reaction is exothermic so increasing temperature shifts equilibrium in the direction that is endothermic ✗ so the value of K_p is increased.✗ ②

(c) Amount of NO_2 converted = $3.00 \times 10^5 - 2.81 \times 10^5$
= 0.19×10^5 Pa
so $P_{N_2O_4} = 0.19 \times 10^5$ Pa ✗
$K_p = 0.19 \times 10^5 \div (2.81 \times 10^5)^2 = 2.40 \times 10^{-7}$ ✓✗ ③

Examiner commentary

① Correct.

② There is not enough detail for the first mark – Tom doesn't give the direction that the equilibrium will shift, and the effect on K_p is incorrect.

③ The calculation includes a common error. He has forgotten that one N_2O_4 is made from 2 NO_2 molecules. He uses this value correctly to calculate K_p but gives no units so loses a mark.

Tom achieves 2 out of 6 marks.

Seren's answer

(a) $K_p = \dfrac{P_{N_2O_4}}{P_{NO_2}^{2}}$ ✓ ①

(b) The reaction is exothermic so increasing temperature shifts equilibrium to left as this direction is endothermic ✓ so the value of K_p is decreased as the amount of product is decreased. ✓ ②

(c) Amount of NO_2 converted = $3.00 \times 10^5 - 2.81 \times 10^5$
= 0.19×10^5 Pa
$P_{N_2O_4} = 9.5 \times 10^3$ Pa ✓
$K_p = 9.5 \times 10^3 \div (2.81 \times 10^5)^2 = 1.20 \times 10^{-7}$ ✓
Units = Pa^{-1} ✓ ③

Examiner commentary

① Correct.

② A full explanation gains both marks.

③ Seren has noticed that one N_2O_4 is made from 2 NO_2 molecules, so there will be half as much N_2O_4 as the NO_2 that is used up. She uses this value correctly to calculate K_p and its units.

Seren achieves 6 out of 6 marks.

Acids and pH

19
Methanoic acid, HCOOH, is a weak acid.

(a) Explain what is meant by the term *weak acid*. [1]

(b) Write an expression for K_a for this acid. [1]

(c) The pH for a solution of methanoic acid is 2.35.

   (i) Calculate the concentration of H^+ ions in this solution. [2]

   (ii) The concentration of the acid in solution is 0.12 mol dm^{-3}.
Calculate the K_a of methanoic acid, giving its units. [2]

(d) When methanoic acid reacts with ammonia, it undergoes the following reaction:

$$HCOOH\ (aq) + NH_3\ (aq) \rightleftharpoons NH_4^+\ (aq) + HCOO^-\ (aq)$$

Identify every molecule that behaves as a base in this equation, explaining your answer. [2]

Tom's answer

(a) A weak acid is one that dissociates partially. ✗ ①

(b) $K_a = \dfrac{[H^+]\ [HCOO^-]}{[HCOOH]}$ ✓ ②

(c) (i) pH = – log[H⁺] ✓ ③
   [H⁺] = 4.47 × 10⁻³ mol dm⁻³ ✓

   (ii) K_a = 4.47 × 10⁻³ ÷ 0.12 ✗ ④
   K_a = 3.73 × 10⁻² mol dm⁻³ ✓

(d) Bases are substances that react with acids so the only base in this case is NH₃. ✗✗ ⑤

Examiner commentary
① Tom fails to indicate what is meant by the 'acid' part of 'weak acid'.
② ③ Both correct.
④ Calculated incorrectly but the units are correct.
⑤ Tom fails to indicate both bases clearly, or explain why there are two bases.
Tom achieves 4 out of 8 marks.

Seren's answer

(a) A weak acid is one that releases H⁺ in a reversible reaction so not all the possible H⁺ are released. ✓ ①

(b) $K_a = \dfrac{[H^+]\ [HCOO^-]}{[HCOOH]}$ ✓

(c) (i) pH = – log[H⁺] ✓
   [H⁺] = 4.47 × 10⁻³ mol dm⁻³ ✓

   (ii) K_a = (4.47 × 10⁻³)² ÷ 0.12 ✓
   K_a = 1.67 × 10⁻⁴ ✗ ②

(d) This is a reversible reaction, and both directions are acid-base reactions. In the forward reaction, NH₃ is the base as it accepts a H⁺ from the HCOOH ✓ and in the reverse reaction HCOO⁻ acts as a base as it accepts a H⁺ from the ammonium. ✓ ③

Examiner commentary
① Seren shows an understanding of both 'weak' and 'acid'.
② (b) and (c) are stated and calculated correctly, but a mark is lost for the lack of units.
③ Seren has realised that acid-base reactions include both a base as a reactant and conjugate base in the products and explains this clearly.
Seren achieves 7 out of 8 marks.

Bases and buffers

20 (a) Sodium hydroxide is a strong base. Calculate the pH of a solution of sodium hydroxide of concentration 0.25 mol dm^{-3}. *[2]*

[The ionic product of water, K_w, is 1.00×10^{-14} mol^2 dm^{-6} at 298 K]

(b) A buffer solution was made by adding 19·6 g of sodium 3-chloropropanoate, CH_2ClCH_2COONa, to 1.00 dm^3 of 3-chloropropanoic acid, CH_2ClCH_2COOH, of concentration 0.100 mol dm^{-3} at 298 K.

(K_a for 3-chloropropanoic acid = 7.94×10^{-5} mol dm^{-3} at 298 K)

(i) Calculate the concentration of the sodium 3-chloropropanoate in mol dm^{-3}. *[1]*

(ii) Calculate the pH of the buffer solution at 298 K. *[2]*

(iii) Explain how this aqueous solution of 3-chloropropanoic acid and sodium 3-chloropropanoate can act as a buffer solution when a small amount of acid or alkali is **separately** added to it. *[3]*

Tom's answer

(a) pH = $-\log(0.25) = 0.6$ ✗✗ ①

(b) (i) $M_r = 36 + 35.5 + 4.04 + 32 + 23 = 130.54$
Concentration = $19.6 \div M_r \div 1 = 0.150$ mol dm^{-3} ✓

(ii) $[H^+] = \dfrac{K_a \times [CH_2ClCH_2COOH]}{[CH_2ClCH_2COO^-]}$

$[H^+] = 7.94 \times 10^{-5} \times 0.100 \div 0.150 = 5.29 \times 10^{-5}$ ✓ ②
pH = $-\log(5.29 \times 10^{-5}) = 4.3$ ✓

(iii) The 3-chloropropanoic acid dissociates to release H$^+$ ions:
$CH_2ClCH_2COOH \longrightarrow CH_2ClCH_2COO^- + H^+$ ✗
Adding base will react with the H$^+$ to neutralise it keeping the pH constant. ✗ If you add acid the molecules will react with the CH_2ClCH_2COONa and remove them. ✗ ③

Examiner commentary

① Tom has forgotten that pH relates to [H$^+$] and has incorrectly used [OH$^-$], so gains no marks for part (a).
② Correctly calculated gaining full marks.
③ Shows a lack of understanding of how buffers work. The key concept is the equilibrium and how adding acid and base affects this.

Tom achieves 3 out of 8 marks.

Seren's answer

(a) $K_w = [H^+] \times [OH^-]$
$[H^+] = 1.00 \times 10^{-14} \div 0.25 = 4.00 \times 10^{-14}$ mol dm^{-3} ✓
pH = $-\log[H^+] = -\log 4.00 \times 10^{-14} = 13.4$ ✓

(b) (i) $M_r = 36 + 35.5 + 4.04 + 32 + 23 = 130.54$
Concentration = $19.6 \div M_r \div 1 = 0.150$ mol dm^{-3} ✓

(ii) $K_a = \dfrac{[H^+][A^-]}{[HA]}$
so $[H^+] = K_a \times [HA] \div [A^-]$
$[H^+] = 7.94 \times 10^{-5} \times 0.100 \div 0.150 = 5.29 \times 10^{-5}$ ✓
pH = $-\log(5.29 \times 10^{-5}) = 4.28$ ✓ ①

(iii) The sodium 3-chloropropanoate dissociates completely:
$CH_2ClCH_2COONa \longrightarrow CH_2ClCH_2COO^- + Na^+$
The 3-chloropropanoic acid sets up an equilibrium:
$CH_2ClCH_2COOH \rightleftharpoons CH_2ClCH_2COO^- + H^+$ ✓
Adding acid means that the equilibrium will shift to the left, removing H$^+$ ✓. Adding base will shift the equilibrium in the opposite direction. ✗ ②

Examiner commentary

① Seren has correctly calculated the answers to all parts.
② Seren's explanation of how a buffer works is correct but she lacks enough detail on the effect of adding a base to gain the final mark.

Seren achieves 7 out of 8 marks.

Titrations and buffers

21

The graph shows the change in pH that occurred when aqueous sodium hydroxide of concentration 0.1 mol dm^{-3} was added to 25 cm^3 of aqueous ethanoic acid of concentration 0.1 mol dm^{-3}.

(a) Select, from the table below, the name of an acid-base indicator which is suitable for this titration, giving a reason for your choice. [2]

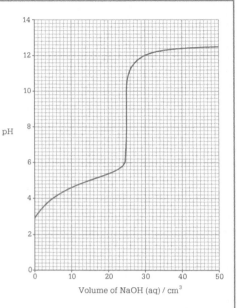

Indicator	Range
Tropaeolin OO	1.3–3.0
Bromocresol green	3.8–5.4
Thymolphthalein	8.3–10.5
Tropaeolin O	11.1–12.7

(b) Sodium ethanoate does not have a pH value of 7.

   (i) State, giving a reason, the pH of aqueous sodium ethanoate. [2]

   (ii) Explain why the pH of aqueous sodium chloride is 7 whilst an aqueous solution of sodium ethanoate is not. [2]

Tom's answer

(a) Thymolphthalein is the right indicator ✓ as it falls in the straight part of the graph. ✗ ①

(b) (i) 9.0 ✓ as this is the endpoint of the titration. ✗ ②

   (ii) Sodium ethanoate releases ethanoate ions when dissolved in water. The ethanoate ions set up an equilibrium by reacting with H⁺ which reduces the concentration of these giving a pH above 7. ✓ ③

Examiner commentary

① Tom has the correct idea; however, he needed to discuss the vertical region not the straight region, and refer to the pH range of the indicator.

② This has the correct pH but 'end point' refers to the indicator colour change and he needed to discuss the formation of the sodium ethanoate in solution.

③ Tom gains the mark for the sodium ethanoate, but he doesn't refer to the sodium chloride.

Tom achieves 3 out of 6 marks.

Seren's answer

(a) Thymolphthalein would work as an indicator ✓ as the range lies completely within the vertical section of the graph. ✓

(b) (i) At the vertical section of the curve, the solution contains only sodium ethanoate. ✓ The midpoint of the vertical section is 9.0 ✓ which gives the pH of this salt.

   (ii) Sodium ethanoate solution contains ethanoate ions, whilst NaCl releases chloride ions. Ethanoic acid is a weak acid, so ethanoate ions remove H⁺ ions in a reversible reaction to form ethanoic acid. ✓ HCl is a strong acid so chloride will not remove H⁺ to form HCl. ✓

Examiner commentary

Seren's answers are clear and complete gaining full marks. She answers concisely but has ensured she answers each part of each question to gain the highest possible marks.

Seren achieves 6 out of 6 marks.

Unit 4 Organic chemistry and analysis

Stereoisomerism

22 (a) (i) State what is meant by the term **stereoisomerism**. *[1]*

(ii) *E-Z* isomerism is one form of stereoisomerism. Compound T is the *Z*-form.

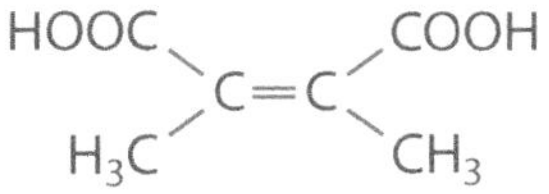

HOOC   COOH
   \   /
    C=C   Compound T
   /   \
H₃C   CH₃

Draw the structural formula of the *E*-form. *[1]*

(iii) Draw the structural formula of an isomer of compound T that is an ester. *[1]*

(iv) Optical isomerism is another type of stereoisomerism.

State what is meant by the term **enantiomer** and describe how enantiomers affect the plane of plane polarised light. *[2]*

(v) The formula of compound K, shown below, contains two chiral centres.

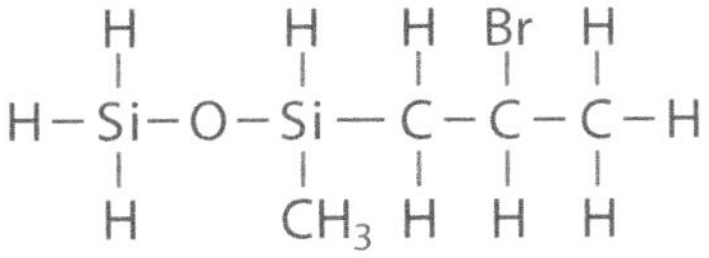

```
     H        H   H  Br  H
     |        |   |  |   |
H — Si — O — Si — C — C — C — H
     |        |   |  |   |
     H       CH₃  H  H   H
```

Identify these chiral centres by putting an asterisk (*) on the appropriate atoms. *[2]*

(b) State the names of reagents A, B and C in the reaction sequence below. *[3]*

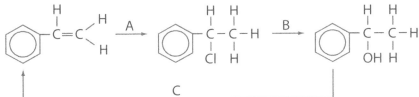

(c) Describe what is observed when 4-bromophenol reacts with aqueous bromine and name the organic product of the reaction. *[3]*

Tom's answer

(a) (i) Isomerism where the molecular formula is the same but different positions are taken up in space. ✗ ①

(ii)

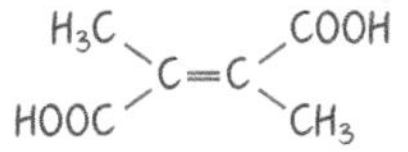

H₃C and COOH on top, HOOC and CH₃ with C=C ✓

(iii)

✓

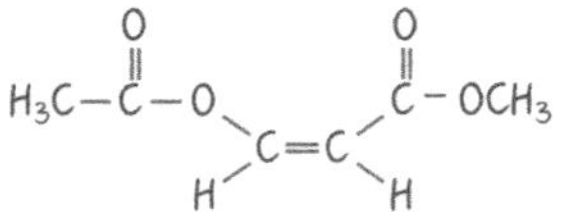

(iv) Isomers that rotate plane polarised light in opposite directions ✓ ②

(v)

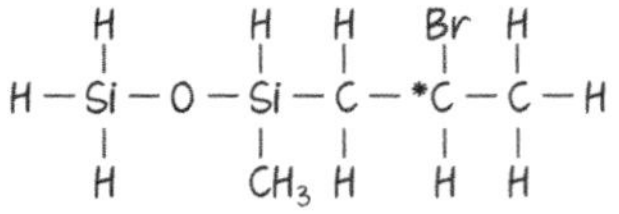

✗ ③

(b) A→Cl_2 ✗ B→aq KOH ✓ C→conc. H_2SO_4 ✓ ④

(c) 2,4,6–Tribromophenol ✓ is formed a solid ✗ ⑤

Examiner commentary

① This answer could be a description of positional isomerism. There is no mention of the same structural formula.

② There is no mention of mirror image forms – only one mark awarded.

③ Tom has only given one correct chiral centre – both are required for the mark.

④ Correct formulae are acceptable here. Aqueous potassium hydroxide is a correct alternative to sodium hydroxide.

⑤ Tom has not stated the colour of the solid or mentioned decolourisation.

Tom achieves 6 out of 13 marks.

Seren's answer

(a) (i) A form of isomerism where the compound has the same structural formula but the atoms take up different positions in space. ✓

(ii)

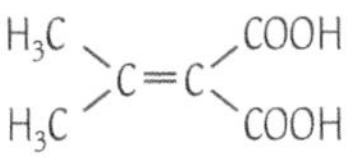

✗ ①

(iii)

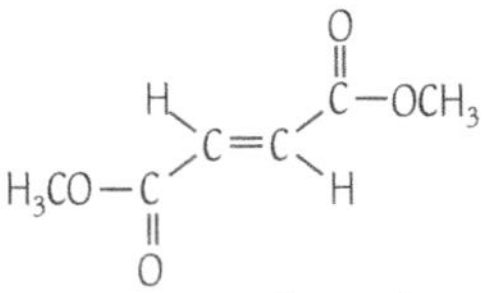

✓

(iv) Mirror image forms that rotate the plane of polarised light ✓ ②

(v)

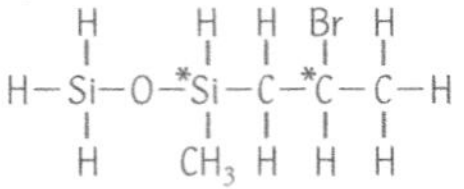

✓

(b) A→HCl ✓ B→aq NaOH ✓ C→conc. sulfuric acid ✓ ③

(c) Bromine water is decolourised ✓ and a white precipitate ✓ of 2,4,6-tribromophenol is produced ✓ ④

Examiner commentary

① The structure is an isomer but is not an E-Z isomer.

② Only one mark here as Seren has not stated in which directions the plane of polarised light is rotated.

③ Names are required but correct formulae are acceptable here.

④ All three required points have been given.

Seren achieves 10 out of 13 marks.

Nitration

23 (a) A student was asked to give the mechanism for the nitration of methyl benzenecarboxylate (methyl benzoate). He wrote the following mechanism.

$$NO_2^+ \qquad H \quad NO_2 \qquad NO_2$$

Point out **three** errors in the answer, explaining your answers as appropriate. *[4]*

(b) Compounds **Q** and **R** are isomers.

compound Q

compound R

(i) State the empirical formula of compounds **Q** and **R**. *[1]*

(ii) State a reagent that will react with compound **Q** but not with compound **R**, giving the result of the test. *[2]*

Tom's answer

(a) The arrow should go from the electron rich ring ✓ to the electrophile. ✓ ①

(b) (i) $C_8H_8O_2$ ✗ ②

   (ii) Sodium carbonate ✓, gas evolved that turns lime water milky. ✓

Seren's answer

(a) The arrow should go from the ring towards the NO_2^+. ✓
The ring is electron rich and can act as a nucleophile ✓.
The product given is the 2-isomer but the mechanism indicates that it should be the 3-isomer. ✓ ①

(b) (i) C_4H_4O ✓

   (ii) Sodium hydrogencarbonate ✓ ②, effervescence will be seen ✓ ③.

Examiner commentary

① Tom has gained 2 of the 4 marks. In the intermediate stage the arrow should come from the bond to hydrogen not the bond to the nitro group. He has also has not realised that the wrong isomer has been produced.

② The molecular formula has been given rather than the empirical formula.

Tom achieves 4 out of 7 marks.

Examiner commentary

① Seren has gained 3 of the 4 marks but has not realised that the wrong bond (from the ring to the nitro group) has been broken in the second stage.

② Both sodium carbonate and sodium hydrogencarbonate are acceptable answers.

③ 'Effervescence' also gives the result of the test. It is not necessary to identify the gas as this has not been requested.

Seren achieves 6 out of 7 marks.

Benzene structure

24 Benzene was first isolated by Faraday in 1825 from the gas that was being used for lighting.

Kekulé suggested that benzene had a six-membered ring structure with an alternating pattern of double and single carbon-to-carbon bonds.

Discuss the currently accepted structure and bonding of benzene, and the evidence that suggests that Kekulé's structure is incorrect. As part of your answer you should comment on why benzene readily undergoes substitution reactions but is resistant to addition. *[6]*

Indicative content

① If the Kekulé formula was correct then it should decolourise bromine water (as addition occurs). ② This decolourisation does not occur. ③ The accepted structure of benzene is that it is a planar molecule with a hexagonal ring of carbon-to-carbon sigma bonds. ④ In addition the *p*-electrons of each carbon atom overlap, ⑤ to form a delocalised structure of electrons / π – structure. ⑥ The enthalpy of hydrogenation of benzene is considerably less than the value that should be obtained if benzene had the Kekulé structure. ⑦ Benzene readily undergoes substitution reactions because this maintains the stable electron ring structure. ⑧ In addition, more energy would be needed to 'destroy' the delocalised ring structure.

5–6 marks

The response given shows a clear and detailed knowledge of the structure of benzene.

The candidate constructs a relevant and logically structured account including all key elements of the indicative content. Scientific conventions and vocabulary are used accurately throughout.

3–4 marks

The response shows a sound understanding of the structure of benzene with some details omitted.

The candidate constructs a logically structured account including the main elements of the indicative content. The use of scientific conventions and vocabulary are generally sound.

1–2 marks

The response shows only an outline understanding of the structure of benzene with a number of points omitted.

The candidate has given a basic account of the structure of benzene but a number of key points are missing. There is some evidence of the correct use of scientific conventions and vocabulary.

0 marks

The candidate does not make any attempt or give an answer worthy of credit.

Tom's answer

Benzene consists of a 6-membered ring of sigma covalent bonds between carbon atoms. ✓ ③. In addition it has a delocalised system ✓ ⑤ (a π-system) of overlapping *p*-electrons ✓ ④. It undergoes substitution reactions related to the stability of the ring as this retains the more stable ring structure. ✓ ⑦.

Examiner commentary

① No comment has been made to discredit the Kekulé structure by means of, for example, adding aqueous bromine or potassium manganate(VII) solution.

② There is no comment as to any observations if aqueous bromine or potassium manganate(VII) solution were added.

⑥ There is no reference to the enthalpies of hydrogenation.

⑧ Although reference has been given to the stability of the ring system, Tom has not gone on to write that more energy is required for addition reactions than for substitution reactions.

Tom has only provided the basic details of the structure of benzene. He has not given any information relating to the stability of the benzene ring.

Tom achieves 3 out of 6 marks.

Seren's answer

The C=C double bonds in the Kekulé structure suggest that it should react with aqueous bromine ✗ ①, this does not occur ✓ ②. Benzene contains a delocalised ring system of overlapping *p*-electrons ✓✓ ④, ⑤. The enthalpy of hydrogenation is 208 kJ mol⁻¹, less than the 360 kJ mol⁻¹ that would be obtained if benzene had the Kekulé structure. ✓ ⑥. The delocalised structure of benzene is therefore more stable than the double / single alternating system of carbon–carbon bonds. ✓ ⑦

Examiner commentary

① Seren has not stated what would be observed if benzene did react with aqueous bromine.

Seren has given a sound answer but has not fully described the structure of benzene. In addition she has not stated that more energy would be needed if benzene underwent addition reactions rather than substitution reactions.

Seren achieves 4 out of 6 marks

Nitromethylbenzenes

25 (a) The nitration of methylbenzene gives two yellow liquids, 1-methyl-2-nitrobenzene and 1-methyl-4-nitrobenzene. This reaction uses the same nitrating agents as when benzene itself is nitrated.

    (i) State the name of the two reagents used to nitrate methylbenzene. *[1]*

    (ii) The boiling temperatures of the organic reactant and products are

compound	boiling temperature / °C
methylbenzene	111
1-methyl-2-nitrobenzene	225
1-methyl-4-nitrobenzene	238

    Suggest a method that could be used to separate these three liquids from the reaction mixture. *[1]*

    (iii) State the molecular formula of 1-methyl-2-nitrobenzene. *[1]*

(b) (i) 1-Methyl-4-nitrobenzene can be oxidised to 4-nitrobenzenecarboxylic acid.

    State the name of a suitable oxidising agent for this reaction. *[1]*

    (ii) Pure 4-nitrobenzenecarboxylic acid is a solid with a melting temperature of 240°C.

    State how this melting temperature might change (if at all), if the acid was impure. *[2]*

    (iii) The impure acid contains small traces of compound Y, which produces a silver mirror with Tollens' reagent. The relative molecular mass of Compound Y is 151.

    Deduce a name for compound Y, giving reasons for your answer. *[4]*

Tom's answer

(a) (i) Nitric acid ✗ ①

    (ii) Fractional distillation ✓

    (iii) $C_7H_7O_2N$ ✓ ②

(b) (i) No response

    (ii) it would melt at a range of temperatures below 240°C. ✓✓ ③

    (iii) CHO ✓④

Examiner commentary

① Only one acid has been mentioned.

② A correct order is not necessary

③ Both responses are correct

④ Tom has only given the formula of the correct compound. A correct formula is acceptable but there is no reasoning for his answer.

Tom achieves 5 marks out of 10.

Seren's answer

(a) (i) Nitric and sulfuric acids ✓ ①

    (ii) Distillation ✗ ②

    (iii) $C_7H_7NO_2$ ✓

(b) (i) Alkaline potassium manganate(VII) ✓

    (ii) It would melt at a different temperature and over a range. ✓ ③

    (iii) It must be an aldehyde as it gives a silver mirror. I think that it is 4-nitrobenzaldehyde as this has a molecular formula of $C_7H_5NO_3$ and this has Mr of 151. ✓✓✓ ④

Examiner commentary

① Seren has gained the mark as 'concentrated' is not necessary.

② Fractional distillation is required, the compounds could not be separated by simple distillation.

③ Only one mark here – she has not mentioned that the melting temperature would be lower.

④ She has not stated why the compound is 4-nitrobenzaldehyde and has therefore lost a mark.

Seren achieves 7 marks out of 10.

Alcohols and phenol

26

(a) Complete the table below [4]

name	formula	colour of aqueous solution with Universal Indicator
phenol	C_6H_5OH	
butan-2-ol		green
	$CH_3(CH_2)_3COOH$	

(b) An alcohol **K** is oxidised to a ketone. The mass of 0.20 mole of this ketone is 17.2 g.

   (i) Calculate the relative molecular mass of the ketone. [1]

   (ii) Deduce a molecular formula for the ketone. [2]

   (iii) Deduce a structural formula for the alcohol, explaining your answer. [3]

Tom's answer

(a)

–	–	red ✗ ①
–	$CH_3CH(OH)CH_3$ ✗ ②	–
pentanoic acid ✓	–	red ✓

(b) (i) M_r is 86 ✓

   (ii) Ketone is R–C(O)–R' M_r of R and R' is
86 – 28 = 58 ✓ C_4H_{10}, so $C_5H_{10}O$ ✓

   (iii) Alcohol must be CH(OH) + R + R' ✓ ③ could be
$CH_3CH_2CH(OH)CH_2CH_2$ ✗ ④

Seren's answer

(a)

–	–	orange ✓
–	$CH_3(CH_2)_2CH_2OH$ ✗ ①	–
pentanoic acid ✓	–	orange ✗ ②

(i) $M_r = \dfrac{mass}{moles}$ $M_r = \dfrac{17.2}{0.2} = 86$ ✓

(ii) A ketone is R – C(O) – R' M_r of R and R' is
86 – (12 + 16) = 58 ✓ this is C_4H_{10}, so $C_5H_{10}O$ ✓

(iii) It must be a secondary alcohol ✓ ie - CH(OH) ✓
and could be $CH_3CH_2CH(OH)CH_2CH_3$ ✓ ③

Examiner commentary

① Phenol is not acidic enough to turn Universal Indicator to red – there should be a distinction between the colour given by phenol and a carboxylic acid.

② Tom has given the formula of the wrong alcohol. He has given propan-2-ol instead of butan-2-ol.

③ This arrangement indicates that a secondary alcohol is present.

④ The formula is wrong. A CH_2 group is at the end of the chain instead of a CH_3 group.

Tom has gained 6 marks out 10.

Examiner commentary

① Seren has given the formula for butan-1-ol not butan-2-ol.

② An acid will give a red colour with Universal Indicator.

③ There is no requirement to name the alcohol.

Seren has gained 8 marks out of 10.

Alcohols and elimination

27 (a) Propan-1-ol is a primary alcohol.

$$H - \overset{\overset{\displaystyle H}{|}}{\underset{\underset{\displaystyle H}{|}}{C}} - \overset{\overset{\displaystyle H}{|}}{\underset{\underset{\displaystyle H}{|}}{C}} - \overset{\overset{\displaystyle H}{|}}{\underset{\underset{\displaystyle H}{|}}{C}} - OH$$

(i) Give the structural formula of two isomers of propan-1-ol. [2]

(ii) State why propan-1-ol does not undergo the triiodomethane (iodoform) reaction. [1]

(iii) Propan-1-ol undergoes an elimination reaction when it is heated with an excess of concentrated sulfuric acid. Give the name of the gaseous organic product and state why this reaction is described as elimination. [2]

(iv) A different organic compound is produced when an excess of propan-1-ol is heated with concentrated sulfuric acid. This product has a relative molecular mass of 102 and contains 15.7% of oxygen by mass, the remainder being carbon and hydrogen. Use the information to suggest a structural formula for this compound, showing all your working. [5]

Tom's answer

(a) (i)

$$H - \overset{\overset{H}{|}}{\underset{\underset{H}{|}}{C}} - \overset{\overset{OH}{|}}{\underset{\underset{H}{|}}{C}} - \overset{\overset{H}{|}}{\underset{\underset{H}{|}}{C}} - H \qquad H - \overset{\overset{H}{|}}{\underset{\underset{H}{|}}{C}} - O - \overset{\overset{H}{|}}{\underset{\underset{H}{|}}{C}} - \overset{\overset{H}{|}}{\underset{\underset{H}{|}}{C}} - H \qquad ✗✓ ①$$

(ii) It does not contain the $CH_3CH_2(OH)^-$ linkage ✗ ②

(iii) Propene ✓ Water is lost ✓

(iv) $\dfrac{15.7 \times 102}{100} = 16$ ✓ = 1 oxygen atom ✓

M_r of $C_xH_y = 102 - 16 = 86$ ✓ structure must be

$$H - \overset{\overset{H}{|}}{\underset{\underset{H}{|}}{C}} - \overset{\overset{H}{|}}{\underset{\underset{H}{|}}{C}} - \overset{\overset{H}{|}}{\underset{\underset{H}{|}}{C}} - O - \overset{\overset{H}{|}}{\underset{\underset{H}{|}}{C}} - \overset{\overset{H}{|}}{\underset{\underset{H}{|}}{C}} - \overset{\overset{H}{|}}{\underset{\underset{H}{|}}{C}} - H \qquad ✓ ③$$

Examiner commentary

① Although this is an isomer of propan-1-ol, the bond to the leads to the hydrogen atom, rather than the oxygen OH group atom. This has therefore been marked wrong.

② The linkage has a $-CH_2(OH)-$ group rather than a $-CH(OH)-$ group.

③ There is a stage missing. Tom has not shown that an 'M_r' of 86 could be C_6H_{14}. This is seen in the answer but candidates have been asked to show all the working.

Tom achieves 7 out of 10 marks.

Seren's answer

(a) (i)

$$H - \overset{\overset{H}{|}}{\underset{\underset{H}{|}}{C}} - \overset{\overset{OH}{|}}{\underset{\underset{H}{|}}{C}} - \overset{\overset{H}{|}}{\underset{\underset{H}{|}}{C}} - H \qquad H - \overset{\overset{H}{|}}{\underset{\underset{H}{|}}{C}} - O - \overset{\overset{H}{|}}{\underset{\underset{H}{|}}{C}} - \overset{\overset{H}{|}}{\underset{\underset{H}{|}}{C}} - H \qquad ✓✓$$

(ii) t does not contain the $CH_3CH(OH)^-$ linkage ✓

(iii) Propylene ✓ ① A molecule splitting into two new molecules. ✗ ②

(iv) M_r is 102 and % oxygen is 15.7. If M_r was 100, % oxygen is 16 ✓ therefore only 1 oxygen atom ✓ M_r C_xH_y must be $102 - 16 = 86$ ✓ therefore C_6H_{14} ✓ ③

$$H - \overset{\overset{H}{|}}{\underset{\underset{H}{|}}{C}} - \overset{\overset{H}{|}}{\underset{\underset{H}{|}}{C}} - \overset{\overset{H}{|}}{\underset{\underset{H}{|}}{C}} - O - \overset{\overset{H}{|}}{\underset{\underset{H}{|}}{C}} - \overset{\overset{H}{|}}{\underset{\underset{H}{|}}{C}} - \overset{\overset{H}{|}}{\underset{\underset{H}{|}}{C}} - H \qquad ✓$$

Examiner commentary

① Seren has given the traditional name for propene, this is acceptable, as the systematic name has not been requested.

② When describing elimination, it is usual to state that a small molecule (water here) has been removed.

③ This is a very clear and precise answer.

Seren achieves 9 out of 10 marks.

Ethanedioic acid

28 (a) Propylamine reacts with ethanedioyl dichloride, $(COCl)_2$, to give compound G that has the molecular formula $C_8H_{16}N_2O_2$,

    (i) Give the structural formula of compound G. *[1]*

    (ii) Compound G is hydrolysed using aqueous sodium hydroxide. The mixture is then acidified and the organic product, ethanedioic acid, is obtained by crystallisation. The ethanedioic acid produced is a hydrate, $(COOH)_2 . xH_2O$, which has a relative molecular mass of 126. Use this information to find the value of x. *[2]*

(b) Ethanedioic acid can be oxidised by acidified potassium manganate (VII) solution. The equation for this reaction shows that 5 moles of ethanedioic acid react with 2 moles of potassium manganate (VII). In a reaction 0.0102 mole of potassium manganate (VII) reacts with 3.57g of impure hydrated ethanedioic acid, M_r 126. Calculate the percentage purity of the impure ethanedioic acid. *[3]*

(c) Ethanamide, C_2H_5NO, contains a peptide linkage.

    (i) Write the structural formula of peptide linkage. *[1]*

    (ii) Write the structural formula of an isomer of ethanamide that does **not** contain a peptide linkage.

Tom's answer

(a) (i)

    ✗ ①

(ii) $(COOH)_2 . xH_2O \rightarrow 126$ M_r of the 'water'
         90   = 126 – 90 = 36
                           x = 36/2 = 2 ✓✓

(b) Number of moles of $(COOH)_2.xH_2O$ = 0.0102 x 2.5
                             = 0.0255 ✓

Mass of acid = 0.0255x126 = 3.21g ✓
% purity = 3.21 x 100 /3.57 = 90 ✓ ②

(c) (i)   ✓   (ii)   ✗ ③

Examiner commentary

① Tom has given a structure that does not fit the molecular formula provided.

② The question does not ask for significant figures and so 90 is acceptable.

③ The structure is wrong and shows a three valent oxygen atom, as well as other errors.

Tom achieves 6 out of 8 marks.

Seren's answer

(a) (i)   ✓

(ii) $(COOH)_2 . xH_2O \rightarrow 120$ therefore
         90   M_r xH_2O = 120 – 90 = 30
                     x = 30/2 = ~ 2 ✓ ①

(b) Number of moles of $(COOH)_2.xH_2O$ = 0.0102 x 5/2 = 0.0255 ✓ therefore mass= 0.0255x126 = 3.21g ✓
% purity = 3.21 x 100/3.57 = 89.9 ✓

(c) (i)   ✓

(ii)   ✓

Examiner commentary

① Seren has wrongly used 120 as the relative molecular mass of the hydrate. The method is correct but a mark has been lost as a result

Seren scores 7 out of 8 marks.

Acids and Esters

29 (a) Compounds K, L, M, N and P are all isomers.

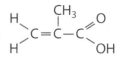

compound K   compound L   compound M

compound N   compound P

(i) State, giving a reason, which of these compounds can be hydrolysed to give a carboxylic acid of relative molecular mass 60, as one of the products. *[2]*

(ii) Compound P can be fully oxidised to a carboxylic acid. State a suitable oxidising agent for this reaction and give the structural formula of the organic product. *[2]*

(iii) Compound M will produce bubbles of a gas when calcium carbonate is added to its aqueous solution. Explain why this occurs. *[3]*

(iv) Explain why the boiling temperature of compound K is likely to be higher than the boiling temperature of compound L. You may use a diagram in your answer. A detailed response is not required. *[4]*

Tom's answer

(i) Compound N as this gives ethanoic acid, M_r 60, on hydrolysis ✓✓

(ii) Acidified dichromate ✓

✗ ①

(iii) For it to react in this way it must be an acid, giving carbon dioxide ✓✓ ②

(iv) Hydrogen bonding ✓

✓ ③

Examiner commentary

① Tom has not oxidised both the alcohol group and the aldehyde group and therefore given the wrong compound.

② He has missed writing that carboxylic acids produce hydrogen ions, H_3O^+, in aqueous solution.

③ Mention of dipole-dipole bonding is missing and there is no reference to the increased amount of energy needed to separate the molecules.

Tom achieves 7 out of 11 marks.

Seren's answer

(a) (i) Compound L as this gives CH_3COOH on hydrolysis. ✗✗ ①
(ii) H^+/MnO_4^- ✓   H\C=C/COOH ✓ ②
                        H/   \COOH

(iii) Needs to be an acid ✓ these give H_3O^+ ions in solution ✓ ③
(iv) Both compounds have dipole-dipole bonding between molecules ✓
Hydrogen bonding is also present ✓

H\   CH₃ O   O   CH₃ H
  C=C—C   ....   C=C—C   ✗ ④
H/   \OH   HO/   \H

More energy is needed to break these bonds between molecules ✓

Examiner commentary

① Compound L does not give ethanoic acid on hydrolysis.
② –COOH is acceptable as the structural formula for a carboxylic acid group.
③ There is no mention of the gas being CO_2.
④ The diagram wrongly shows hydrogen bonding between two hydrogen atoms.
Seren achieves 7 out of 11 marks.

Preparation of alcohols

30 (a) One method of preparing pentan-3-ol is by the reduction of pentan-3-one.

(i) State the name of a reducing agent that can be used for this reaction. [1]

(ii) An infrared spectrum was taken of a sample of pentan-3-ol made in this way.
Describe how this could be used to see if any pentan-3-one remained. [2]

(iii) State how a gas-liquid chromatogram of this sample would show that an impurity was present. [1]

(b) Pentan-3-ol can also be produced by the hydrolysis of 3-pentyl ethanoate, $CH_3COOCH(CH_2CH_3)_2$.

(i) Give the equation for the hydrolysis of 3-pentyl ethanoate using water as the other reactant. [2]

(ii) State why aqueous sodium hydroxide is often used instead of water in this reaction. [1]

(iii) The hydrolysis of pentyl ethanoate involves heterolytic bond fission. State what is meant by the term '**heterolytic bond fission**'. [1]

Tom's answer

(a) (i) Lithium aluminium hydride. ✓ ①
(ii) If pentan-3-one was present I would see an extra peak at 1750 cm⁻¹. This is due to the C=O bond. ✓✓ ②
(iii) I would see several peaks. ✗ ③
(b) (i) $CH_3COOCH(CH_2CH_3)_2 + 2H_2O \rightarrow$
$CH_3COOH + (CH_3CH_2)_2CHOH$ ✓ ④
(ii) It is less dangerous. ✗ ⑤
(iii) A form of bonding where each atom receives back its own electron ✗ ⑥

Examiner commentary

① Lithium aluminium hydride is an alternative answer.
② Tom has given the correct peak and identified it – two marks.
③ 'Several' peaks means more than two – therefore wrong.
④ Only one mark here as the formulae are correct but the balancing is wrong.
⑤ The use of aqueous sodium hydroxide is actually more hazardous than using water – no mark given.
⑥ Tom has described homolytic fission, rather than heterolytic fission.
Tom achieves 4 marks out of 8.

Seren's answer

(a) (i) Sodium tetrahydridoborate(III). ✓

(ii) If pentan-3-one was present I would see an extra peak at 1750 cm⁻¹. ✓ ①

(iii) An extra peak would be seen. ✓ ②

(b) (i) $CH_3COOCH(CH_2CH_3)_2 + H_2O$
$\rightarrow CH_3COOH + (CH_3CH_2)_2CHOH$ ✓✓ ③

(ii) The hydrolysis of the ester occurs at a faster rate. ✓ ④

(iii) A process of bond breaking where oppositely charged ions are produced. ✓ ⑤

Examiner commentary

① Seren has only gained one mark as she has not identified the peak at 1750 cm⁻¹.

② She has realised that the chromatogram would show an extra peak (due to the impurity).

③ The equation has gained both marks – one for the correct formulae and one for it being correctly balanced.

④ The reaction rate is correctly described as increasing.

⑤ She has given an accurate definition of heterolytic fission.

Seren achieves 7 out of 8 marks.

Diazonium compounds

31 The red dye, Sudan I, has been used illegally as a food dye. This dye is made by reacting together benzenediazonium chloride and naphthalen-2-ol.

(i) Complete the sentences below, which describe the preparation of benzenediazonium chloride.

Benzenediazonium chloride is made by reacting phenylamine with _____ at a temperature of _____°C. If the reaction temperature rises the diazonium compound may decompose giving _____ and bubbles of _____ gas. [4]

(ii) Sudan I is then made by adding a solution of naphthalen-2-ol to the prepared solution of benzenediazonium chloride. The mixture needs to be at a pH of ____ [1]

(iii) Jessica made some Sudan I by the method above. She found that her yield of the red dye was more than 100%. Suggest two reasons for this yield, apart from errors in calculating the yield. [2]

(iv) When Tom made some Sudan I by the same method he found that his yield was only 57%. Suggest two reasons why errors in his practical work could give this low yield. [2]

Tom's answer

(i) Sodium nitrite / hydrochloric acid ✓ ①
10°C ✓ phenol ✓ carbon dioxide ✗ ②

(ii) 4 ✗ ③

(iii) Some was lost from the filter paper before weighing ✗ ✗ ④

(iv) He let the mixture warm up and some decomposition occurred. ✓✗ ⑤

Examiner commentary

① Nitrous acid is made 'in situ' from sodium nitrite and hydrochloric acid, and this answer is acceptable.

② Nitrogen is evolved – carbon dioxide is wrong.

③ The mixture needs to be alkaline not acidic.

④ Only one answer has been given. If some material was lost before weighing, then the yield would have been reduced, not increased.

⑤ Only one answer has been given. The answer to (iii) would have been appropriate here.

Tom achieves 4 out of 9 marks.

Seren's answer

(i) <u>nitrous acid</u> ✓ <u>5°C</u> ✓ _____ ✗ ①
    <u>nitrogen</u> ✓

(ii) 7 ✗ ②

(iii) Jessica started with too large a quantity. ✓
     Her product was still damp. ✓

(iv) The temperature was too warm and the
     diazonium compound decomposed ✓ ✗ ③

Examiner commentary

① Seren has not mentioned that phenol is a product when the benzenediazonium compound decomposes on warming.

② Azo dyes, such as Sudan I, are made by treating the diazonium compound with a phenol (or amine) in an alkaline solution. The pH needs to be greater than 7.

③ Only one answer has been given. Another correct response would be that some material was lost during filtration.

Seren achieves 6 out of 9 marks.

(Chloromethyl)benzene

Q & A 32

A student makes phenylmethanol, $C_6H_5CH_2OH$, from methylbenzene in two stages.

$$C_6H_5CH_3 \longrightarrow C_6H_5CH_2Cl \longrightarrow C_6H_5CH_2OH$$
$$\text{(chloromethyl)benzene}$$

(a) (Chloromethyl)benzene is produced from methylbenzene by reacting it with chlorine, in a radical substitution reaction.

    (i) Write an equation that shows chlorine, Cl_2, undergoing homolytic fission. *[1]*

    (ii) Calculate the percentage increase in mass of the organic compounds that would occur if 1 mole of methylbenzene is converted to 1 mole of (chloromethyl)benzene. *[2]*

    (iii) State the name of a reagent that would be used to convert (chloromethyl)benzene to phenylmethanol in the second stage of the reaction. *[1]*

(b) When (chloromethyl)benzene, M_r 126.5, is made from methylbenzene and chlorine, it can be contaminated with traces of other compounds. One of these contaminants contains only C, H and Cl and has an M_r of 161. Suggest a molecular and structural formula for this contaminant and the name and type of mechanism that has given this contaminant. *[4]*

Tom's answer

(a) (i) $Cl–Cl \rightarrow Cl^{\cdot} + Cl^{-}$ ✗ ①

    (ii) increase in M_r 126.5–92 =
     33.5 × % increase in mass
     = 36.4 ✓ ②

    (iii) sodium hydroxide ✓ ③

(b)
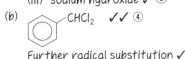

Further radical substitution ✓

Examiner commentary

① The equation wrongly shows heterolytic fission.

② The subtraction has been done incorrectly. However, the percentage has been carried out correctly based on 33.5. A mark has been awarded for 'error carried forward'.

③ The question asks for the name of the reagent – Tom has not stated that aqueous conditions are needed but has been given the benefit of doubt.

④ The correct structural formula has been given. This formula implies that a further chlorine atom is present and therefore this response is worth two marks. However, the molecular formula has not been provided.

Tom achieves 5 out of 8 marks.

Seren's answer

(a) (i) $Cl_2 \rightarrow 2Cl\cdot$ ✓

    (ii) 37.5 ✓✓ ①

    (iii) aqueous sodium hydroxide ✓

(b) The relatively large increase in Mr suggests that another chlorine atom is present. ✓

Formula is $C_7H_6Cl_2$ ✓

Structural formula is  ✗ ②

Examiner commentary

① The question does not ask candidates to show their working. A correct answer gets both marks.

② Ring substitution does not occur under these conditions. Seren has not suggested the name and type of mechanism.

Seren achieves 6 out of 8 marks.

Butanedione

33 (a) The diagram shows a blank section of the electromagnetic spectrum.

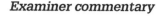

wavelength increasing

    (i) Draw an arrow beneath the diagram to indicate the direction of increasing energy. [1]

    (ii) Write 'infrared', 'ultraviolet' and 'visible' in their correct positions on the diagram. [1]

(b) In white light butanedione is a yellow liquid.

$$H_3C-\overset{\displaystyle O}{\overset{\displaystyle \|}{C}}-\overset{\displaystyle O}{\overset{\displaystyle \|}{C}}-CH_3$$

    (i) State and explain the colour of butanedione in blue light. [2]

    (ii) Elfed reduces butanedione to the colourless liquid butane-2,3-diol. State how he will know when the reaction is complete. [1]

    (iii) State one way in which the reduction in (ii) can be speeded up, without the use of increased heat or the use of a catalyst. [1]

    (iv) Give the structural formula of any isomer of butanedione and state a test that is given by your choice of isomer but not by butanedione. Your answer should mention the reagent used and the result of your test. [3]

Tom's answer

(a) (i) and (ii)

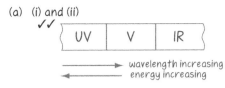

(b) (i)   It will be blue ✗ as blue light is reflected ✗ ①
     (ii) It will all be clear ✗ ②
     (iii) Heat the mixture ✗ ③
     (iv)

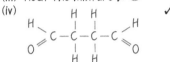

Tollens' reagent ✓ red precipitate ✗ ④

Examiner commentary

① Blue light is absorbed – no marks here.

② Clear does not have the same meaning as 'turns colourless'.

③ The question stated that heat was not acceptable as an answer.

④ The structure given is correct and will react with Tollens' reagent but this reagent gives a silver mirror, not a red precipitate.

Tom achieves 4 out 9 marks.

Seren's answer

(a) (i)   and (ii)

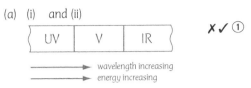

✗✓ ①

(b) (i)   It will appear black ✓ as it absorbs blue light ✓
     (ii) The yellow colour will disappear ✓ ②
     (iii) Make the solution stronger ✓ ③
     (iv)

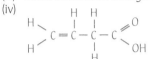

Bromine water ✓ becomes clear ✗ ④

Examiner commentary

① Seren has not realised that energy is inversely proportional to frequency.

② 'Disappear' is acceptable but not as good an answer as 'it becomes colourless'.

③ 'Stronger' is satisfactory but not as acceptable as 'more concentrated'.

④ The structure is correct and it will react with bromine water. However, 'clear' means that you can see through it – it is not the same as 'colourless'.

Seren achieves 7 out of 9 marks.

Structure determination

34

An unlabelled bottle containing a colourless liquid L was found in a laboratory store.

When it was tested the following information was obtained.

- The mass spectrum showed a molecular ion signal at m/z 116 and a strong signal at m/z 85.

- The empirical formula of the compound was C_3H_6O.

- The infrared spectrum showed a strong signal at 1737 cm^{-1} but there was no broad peak at 2500–3550 cm^{-1}.

- The high resolution NMR spectrum is shown below.

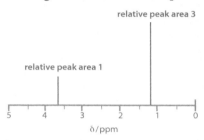

Use all the information to suggest a structural formula for Compound L.   [9]

Mark scheme

① The molecular ion in the mass spectrum indicates that the M_r of compound L is 116.
② This value means that the formula of compound L must be $(C_3H_6O)_n$. M_r C_3H_6O = 58.
n = 116/58 = 2. Molecular formula is $C_6H_{12}O_2$. ③ Since there are two oxygen atoms in a molecule of compound L it must be a carboxylic acid or an ester. ④ The peak at 1737 cm^{-1} in the infrared spectrum indicates that a C=O bond is present. No signal at 2500–3550 cm^{-1} indicates that an O–H bond is absent. ⑤ Compound L cannot therefore be a carboxylic acid. It must be an ester, RCOOR'. ⑥ The mass spectrum signal at 85 indicates a loss of 31 from the molecular ion at 116. This is likely to be a methoxy group / -OCH$_3$. The ester must be a methyl ester / R' is CH$_3$. ⑦ R must have an 'M_r' of 116 – 59 = 57 (where 57 is the 'M_r' of C=O and OCH$_3$). R must be C_4H_9. ⑧ The NMR spectrum has two unsplit signals, which fits with an ester structure as the alkyl groups are not next to each other. The 'butyl' protons must result in the signal at 1.2 δ and contain all equivalent protons. R is $(CH_3)_3C$-. ⑨ Therefore compound L has the structural formula $(CH_3)_3COOCH_3$.

Tom's answer

The relative molecular mass is 116 because the molecular ion indicates the M_r value ✓① 'M_r C_3H_6O = 58, therefore formula is $C_6H_{12}O_2$, as 116 is twice 58 ✓ ② It is an ester as –OH is absent ✓ ⑤ Fragment of 31 is lost, must be –OCH$_3$, therefore RCO/OCH3. ✓ ⑥ The smaller NMR signal must be the methyl group and therefore the other signal must contain 9 protons, therefore C_4H_9 ✓ ⑦ Ester must be $C_4H_9COOCH_3$ ✓ ⑨

Examiner commentary

③ No clear explanation has been given for this marking point.

④ There is no identification of the C=O bond.

⑧ Tom has not stated that all the protons are equivalent in C_4H_9 group.

⑨ The answer for the ester has gained a mark, error carried forward, as the inability to show the structure of the C_4H_9 group has already been penalised.

Tom's answer is well organised but lacks the information to clearly identity the ester.

Tom achieves 6 out of 9 marks.

Seren's answer

The 'M_r' of C_3H_6O is 58 and since the relative molecular mass is 116, the molecular formula must be $C_6H_{12}O_2$ ✓✓ ①,② Compound L must either be an acid or an ester as there two oxygen atoms present ✓ ③ No O-H peak is present as there is no peak at 2500–3550 cm^{-1} but the peak at 1737 cm^{-1} shows that C=O is present ✓ ④ It must be an ester ✓ ⑤ The unsplit NMR signals are in ratio 3:1 and must be 9 protons and 3 protons, therefore must be C_4H_9 and CH$_3$ ✓ ⑦. All the butyl protons are equivalent (no splitting) ✓ ⑧ The ester must be $CH_3COOC(CH_3)_3$ ✓ ⑨

Examiner commentary

⑥ Seren has not deduced that 'Mr' 31 must be OCH$_3$, therefore a methyl ester.

⑨ She has been given this mark for 'error carried forward' as the wrong ester has already been penalised.

This is a very good answer but the failure to identify the methoxy group has meant that she has arrived at the wrong ester.

Seren achieves 8 out of 9 marks.

Quickfire Answers

Unit 3 Physical and Inorganic Chemistry

1 $\underline{S_8}$: S = 0 Fe^{3+}: Fe = +3   NaCl: Na = +1
H_2O: O = −2 F_2O: O = +2 CaH_2: H = −1
$AlCl_4^-$: Al = +3   NaOCl: Cl = +1 $NaIO_3$: I = +5
MnO_4^-: Mn = +7

2

high-resistance voltmeter

V

1 atm H_2 gas

salt bridge

platinum electrodes

1 mol dm^{-3} H^+ (aq)

1 mol dm^{-3} of Fe^{2+} (aq) / 1 mol dm^{-3} of Fe^{3+}

3 a) EMF = 0.34 − (−0.76) = 1.10V
b) EMF = 0.77 − (−0.76) = 1.53V

4 Chlorine has a more positive E^θ value than bromine, which shows that chlorine is a stronger oxidising agent than bromine and can oxidise bromide to bromine. Iodine has a less positive E^θ value than bromine so it cannot oxidise the bromide to Br_2.

5 $2\,MnO_4^- + 16\,H^+ + 10\,Cl^- \rightarrow 2\,Mn^{2+} + 8\,H_2O + 5\,Cl_2$

6 Moles MnO_4^- = 0.200 × 21.40 ÷ 1000
           = 0.00428 moles.
Moles Fe^{2+} = 0.00428 × 5 = 0.0214
Mass Fe = 0.0214 × 55.8 = 1.194g
% by mass = 1.194 ÷ 1.252 × 100 = 95.4%

7 Concentration of Cu^{2+} = 0.248 × 30.25 ÷ 25.00
           = 0.300 mol dm^{-3}

8 As you go down group 4 the stability of the +2 oxidation state increases due to the inert pair effect. Carbon is stable as +4 so CO will be easily oxidised making it a reducing agent.
Lead is stable in the +2 oxidation state so PbO won't be able to reduce other substances as it is stable.

9 Addition of sodium hydroxide to colourless solutions of each will produce a white precipitate in each one. If excess sodium hydroxide is added, the white precipitate remains in the magnesium nitrate sample, but the precipitate dissolves for lead(II) nitrate to leave a colourless solution. The difference is because lead is an amphoteric metal and magnesium is not.

10 $NaHSO_4$
SO_2 – pungent, acidic gas
S – yellow solid
H_2S – rotten egg smell

11 Ti: $1s^2 2s^2 2p^6 3s^2 3p^6 3d^2 4s^2$
Co: $1s^2 2s^2 2p^6 3s^2 3p^6 3d^7 4s^2$
Cr^{3+}: $1s^2 2s^2 2p^6 3s^2 3p^6 3d^3$
Ni^{2+}: $1s^2 2s^2 2p^6 3s^2 3p^6 3d^8$

12 Cu^{2+} (aq) + 2 OH^- (aq) → $Cu(OH)_2$ (s)
Fe^{3+} (aq) + 3 OH^- (aq) → $Fe(OH)_3$ (s)

13 (i) Measure the pressure (at constant volume) over time.
(ii) Measure the volume (at constant pressure) over time.
(iii) Measure colour change by colourimetry over time.

14 Rate = 0.046 ÷ 10 = 0.0046 mol s^{-1}

15 (i) Second order; units of $k = mol^{-1}\ dm^3\ s^{-1}$
(ii) First order; units of $k = s^{-1}$

16 (a) Rate = $k\ [N_2O_5][H_2O]$
(b) $C_4H_9Br + OH^- \rightarrow C_4H_9OH + Br^-$

17 $A = k \div e^{(-E_a/RT)}$ so $A = 1.76 \times 10^3 \div e^{(-66000/8.314 \times 298)} = 6.53 \times 10^{14}$
$k = 6.53 \times 10^{14} \times e^{(-66000/8.314 \times 308)} = 4179\ s^{-1}$

18 $\Delta S = 73 + 214 - 136 = 151\ J\ K^{-1}\ mol^{-1}$

19 $\Delta H = (-416) + (-394) - (-1131) = 321\ kJ\ mol^{-1}$

20 $\Delta G = \Delta H - T\Delta S = 321 - 300 \times (151 \div 1000) = 275.7\ kJ\ mol^{-1}$

21 $T = \Delta H \div \Delta S = 321,000 \div 151 = 2126\ K$

22 $K_p = \dfrac{P_{NO}{}^4 \times P_{H_2O}{}^6}{P_{NH_3}{}^4 \times P_{O_2}{}^5}$

23 If we increase the temperature, then according to Le Chatelier's principle the equilibrium will shift to the endothermic direction. This is a shift to the left, increasing the partial pressure of SO_2 and O_2 and decreasing the partial pressure of SO_3. This will decrease the value of K_p.

24 pH = − log (0.015) = 1.82

25 $[H^+] = 6.31 \times 10^{-4}\ mol\ dm^{-3}$

26 $[H^+] = 2.83 \times 10^{-3}\ mol\ dm^{-3}$ giving a pH of 2.55

27 $K_a = 2.0 \times 10^{-9}\ mol\ dm^{-3}$

28 $[H^+] = 3.33 \times 10^{-14}$ giving a pH of 13.5

29 $[H^+] = 8.0 \times 10^{-6}$ giving a pH of 5.1

Unit 4 Organic Chemistry and Analysis

30

One atom of the double bond has two carbon atoms that are the same.

31

32

33 12.3 g

34

35 3-Methylpentanoic acid

36

37

38 C_4H_4O

39 Pentan-3-one

40 (a)

41 $C_4H_3O_2$

42 Pentane

43 Ethanol and hexanoic acid

44 $C_8H_8O_3$

45 133.5 g

46 3-Methylbutanenitrile

47 (i) Add KCN

(ii) Add $LiAlH_4$ in ethoxyethane

48 Pentylamine

49

50 4.14 g

51 $C_{12}H_{11}N_3$

52 182

53 The colours of the spectrum that are not green – red, orange, blue etc.

54 Only red light can be reflected. If there is no red light to be reflected the flower appears as black.

55 It absorbs green therefore it is purple.

56 2-Aminobutanoic acid

2-Aminopentanoic acid

57

58 $C_6H_{12}O_6$

59 (a) $LiAlH_4$

(b) Concentrated H_2SO_4

60 (a) Water/steam (and phosphoric acid catalyst)

(b) Acidified potassium dichromate

61 X is chloromethane or bromomethane

Y is ethanenitrile

62 Use a water bath or an electrical heater

63 (a) the crystals will not show any yellow colour

(b) the solvent from further washing will be colourless

64 The melting temperature must be above room temperature but the actual value is unknown

65

66

(E)-1-bromo-2-chloroethene   (Z)-1-bromo-2-chloroethene

67 Use a different column

68 Otherwise the mixture would dissolve in the solvent in the beaker

Extra 1

$Al(OH)_3 + 3H^+ \rightarrow Al^{3+} + 3H_2O$ $PbO + 2H^+ \rightarrow Pb^{2+} + H_2O$

$Al(OH)_3 + OH^- \rightarrow [Al(OH)_4]^-$ $PbO + H_2O + 2OH^- \rightarrow [Pb(OH)_4]^-$

Extra 2

$A = \dfrac{k}{e^{-Ea}/RT}$ $E_a = RT \ln (^A/_k)$

$T = Ea/R \ln (^A/_k)$

Extra 3

a) 76.4   b) 27.4 g

Extra 4

a) propan-1-ol   c) It contains a chiral centre

b)

Extra 5

a) cyclohexene   d) pentan-2-one

b) hexanal   e) ethanedioic acid

c) propane-1,2-diol

Index

acid, definition of 38, 60
acid-base 13, 21, 38, 42–43, 67
  equilibrium 38
  properties of oxides 21
  titration 13, 42–43, 67
acidic oxide 21
activation energy 29
addition polymerisation 75
addition reaction 50–51, 64
alcohols, formation
  from aldehydes and ketones 54
  from halogenoalkanes 54
alcohols, oxidation of 57, 61
alcohols, reaction
  with carboxylic acids 55
  with ethanoyl chloride 55
  with hydrogen halides 55
alcohols, relative acidity of 60
aldehydes
  distinguishing from ketones 57
  formation of alcohols from 54
  identifying 59
  oxidation of 61
  reduction of 58
aliphatic amines 65–66
alkaline hydrolysis of chloroalkanes
  and chlorobenzene 53
alkylbenzenes, oxidation of 61
aluminium chloride 18, 52, 72
amines
  aliphatic 65–66
  aromatic 67
  basicity of 65
  coupling reactions 67
  ethanoylation of 66
  formation from nitrobenzenes 65
  primary 65–67
  reaction with cold nitric(III) acid 66
amino acids 49, 69–70, 76
amphoteric 16, 21, 69
aromatic amines 67
aromatic carboxylic acid 61
atom, oxidation state of 8

base, definition of 38
basic oxide 21
benzene
  alkylation of 52, 72
  delocalisation energy of 50
  halogenation of 51–52
  nitration of 51
  resistance to addition reactions 50
  structure of 50

benzenediazonium, coupling
  reactions 67
bidentate 25
bond energy 53
boron nitride 19
  cubic 19
  hexagonal 19
  nanotubes 19
bromination 55
buffer 41

carbonyl compounds
  adding to hydrogen cyanide 58
  also see aldehydes; ketones
carboxylic acids
  aromatic 61
  conversion to acid chlorides 63
  conversion to amides and nitriles 64
  conversion to esters 63
  decarboxylation of 62
  forming 61
  oxidation of 72
  reaction with alcohols 55
  reduction of 62
  relative acidity 60
catalyst 19, 24, 26, 28–29, 36–37,
  51–52, 55, 63, 70, 72
cell diagram, labelling 10
charge 8
chiral centre 49, 58, 69
chlorate, uses of 23
chlorides, reactions with water 21
chlorination 55
chlorine
  reaction with sodium hydroxide 22
  uses of 23
chromatography 78–79
chromophore 67
colour and wavelength 68
complexes
  colours 25
  examples 25
  transition metal 25–26
compound, stability of 31
concentration calculation 15
condensation polymerisation 75
conjugation 68
co-ordinate bond 18, 24–25, 65
coupling reactions 67
covalent bond 17–20, 52–53

d-block 24–26
  electronic configurations 24
  oxidation states 24
  transition metal ions 24
d-orbital 16–17, 21
delocalisation 19–20, 50, 60
dimer 18
dipeptides 69–70
displacement reaction 22
disproportionation 22
dissociation of water 40
distillation 73
donor-acceptor compound 18

E-Z isomerism 48–49
electrochemical cell 9–10
electromagnetic spectrum 68
electron 8–11, 13, 16–20, 24–25,
  50–51, 53, 60, 65, 67
electron deficiency 18, 51
electronic configurations 16, 24
electrophilic substitution 51–52
elements 8, 10, 16–18, 20, 22–24,
  30–32
enantiomer 49
endothermic direction 36
endothermic reaction 32, 36–37
enthalpy change 30–32
enthalpy value 31
entropy change 32
entropy value 32
equilibrium constant 34–40
equilibrium mixture 35
exothermic reaction 32, 36–37

Fehling's reagent 57, 59
fuel cell 12

gas-liquid chromatography (GLC)
  78–79
Gibbs free energy 32–33

half-cell 9–11
half-equation 9, 11, 13
Hess's law 30
heterogeneous catalyst 26
high performance liquid
  chromatography (HPLC) 79
high resolution NMR spectra 77
homogeneous catalyst 26
homologous series 58, 62, 64
hydrogen cyanide, adding to carbonyl
  compounds 58
hydrolysis 53, 58, 63–64, 70
hydroxynitriles, formation of 64

immiscible liquids 73
indicator 42–43
inert pair effect 16–17, 20
insoluble solid separation 73
iodination 55
iodine reduction 15
ionic compound, formation of 31
isoelectronic 19

ketones
    distinguishing from aldehydes 57
    formation of alcohols from 54
    identifying 59
    reduction of 58
    tests for the $CH_3C=O$ group 59

ligand 25
lone pair 18, 21, 25, 53, 65–66

melting temperature 19, 59, 69, 75
miscible liquids 73
mobile phase 79
monodentate 25

nitriles
    conversion of carboxylic acids to 64
    formation of 64
    reduction of 64
nuclear magnetic resonance (NMR)
    spectra 77

octet expansion 17
optical isomerism 49
organic synthesis 12, 71–72
oxidation 8–14, 16–17, 20, 22–24, 26,
    57, 61–62, 71–72
oxidation state 8, 10, 16–17, 20,
    22–24, 26
    of an atom 8
oxidising agent 8, 20, 22–23, 57, 61, 72

p-block 16–23
    electronic configurations 16
    group 3 elements 16, 18–19
    group 4 elements 16, 20–21
    group 7 elements 16, 22–23
    oxidation states 17, 20
p-orbital 16–17
Pb^{2+} 16, 21
partial pressure 34–35
pH 38–43, 60
    of acids 38–39
    of buffers 31
    of salts 43
    of strong bases 40
phenol
    acidity 56, 60
    reactions 56, 67
polarisation 52, 58
polyamides 70, 76
polyesters 76
polypeptides 70
pressure 10, 27, 34–37, 53, 73, 75, 79
proteins 70, 76

racemic mixture 49
radical reaction 71, 75
rate constant 28–29
rate determining step 29
rate equation 28–29, 37
reactant 8, 13, 16, 26–29, 32, 34–37,
    51, 59
reacting ratio 14–15
reaction feasibility 11
reaction orders 28
reaction rate 27–29, 37
redox reaction 8–9, 12–15
    equations 9
    use of 12
redox titration 13–14
reduction 8–9, 11–13, 15, 20, 22–23,
    54, 57–58, 62, 64–65

s-orbital 16–17
shell (of element) 17–19, 21, 24
sodium halides, reaction with
concentrated sulfuric acid 23
sodium hydroxide, reactions with
    transition metal compounds 26
soluble solids from solution 74
solvent extraction 73
standard electrode potential (E)
    10–11, 22
standard hydrogen electrode 10
stereoisomerism 48–49
strong acid-strong base titration
    curve 42
strong acid-weak base titration
    curve 43

temperature 10, 19, 22, 27–29, 32–34,
    36–37, 40, 51–52, 55, 59, 63, 66, 69,
    73–75, 78–79
    effect on rates 29
    melting 19, 59, 69, 75
thin layer chromatography (TLC) 78
titration curve 42–43
Tollens' reagent 57, 59
transition elements 24
transition metals 25–26

volume calculation 15

water, relative acidity of 60